Bread from Stones

Bread from Stones

by Julius Hensel

Foreword by Charles Walters

Afterword by Philip S. Callahan, Ph.D.

Acres U.S.A.
Austin, Texas

Bread from Stones

Acres U.S.A.
P.O. Box 91299
Austin, Texas 78709 U.S.A.
(512) 892-4400 • fax (512) 892-4448
info@acresusa.com • www.acresusa.com

Printed in the United States of America

Publisher's Cataloging-in-Publication

Hensel, Julius.
Bread from stones / Julius Hensel; with a foreword by Charles Walters; and an afterword by Philip S. Callahan. — Austin, TX, ACRES U.S.A., 1991
        xxvi, 102 pp., ill., 23 cm.
        Includes Index
        Includes Bibliography
        ISBN 0-911311-30-0 (trade)

        1. Soil fertility. 2. Fertilizers. 3. Plants — nutrition.
4. Agriculture — United States. I. Hensel, Julius. II. Title.

        S633 .H48 1991   631.8 20

*Dedicated to the memory of Larry Ephron,
a scientist who made the connection
between bread and stones.*

Perhaps when we give ear more attentively to the voice of the soil reporting the ecological array of the different life forms (microbes, plants, animals, and man) over the earth, we shall recognize the soil fertility—according to the rocks and resulting soil in their climatic settings—playing the major role through food quality rather than quantity, surpluses, prices, etc., in determining those respective arrays. Man still refuses to see himself under control by the soil. Then when we take national inventory of the reserves of fertility in the rocks and minerals mobilized so slowly into agricultural production in contrast to the speed of exploitation of virgin and remaining soil fertility, perhaps thrift and conservatism with reference to the mineral resources of our soils will be the first and foremost feature of our agricultural policy. By that policy we shall build the best national defense, if there is any basis for contending that if wars must come, food will win them and write the peace. May rocks their silence break and speak nationally through a better knowledge of soil for food as the basis of national health and thereby a national strength for the prevention of war and for the simplest road to peace. Our future national strength must rest in our soils.—*William A. Albrecht*, writing in *Let Rocks Their Silence Break* published in *The Albrecht Papers, Volume I.*

CONTENTS

A WORD FROM THE PUBLISHER

It has been almost twenty years since *Acres U.S.A.* reported on *Mineralization, a New Basis for Proper Nutrition*, by Albert Carter Savage. While I was visiting with that late great scientist, he mentioned the granddaddy of all studies on mineralization, *Bread from Stones*, which is now the first entry in the *Acres U.S.A.* Classics Series. Albert Carter Savage was more than a soil scientist. He was also a geologist. During the 1930s he discovered a balanced concoction based on the simplest of rocks, all of which were available near Lexington, Kentucky. The rocks were Kentucky Devonian oil shale, potash marl, secondary fossiliferous limestone (famous for making race horses fast and strong) and raw rock phosphate. These, in combination with manure or compost, provided a powerful fix for the soil and those who ate the food from it.

Bread from Stones, then as now, rated attention as a classic, for it explains in understandable terms the role of earth minerals in food production. And yet it calls for an overview generally missing when we look at soil systems.

Happily, that overview has been supplied by John D. Hamaker and Don Weaver, who take us back to the "beginning" the way James Michener does in his doorstopper novels.

The synopsis that follows was drawn from *The Survival of Civilization*, by Hamaker and Weaver in April 1982, and the *Comment* papers in Weaver's updating bulletins, numbers one to ten. The synopsis has been prepared to draw attention to the two neglected factors which, when understood, make it easy to understand long-term climate. It also makes clear the urgent need for action if we are to have a chance to affect our survival by continuing to make bread from stones.

There exists today a fatal lack of understanding of the soil system, and therefore of the climate system. As a result, none of the things are being done that ought to be done in response to the problem. Perhaps a new perspective will clear up our confusion.

All living organisms are a part of a dynamic process of cycling the gases and minerals which are in combined form in the rocks of the earth's mantle and in the ocean floor. The gases and minerals are separated by heat and pressure in that part of the tectonic system where the energy is released to run the system. Those minerals from which the gases have been extracted are ejected into the mountains, and the gases are ejected into the atmosphere. The living organisms recombine the gases and minerals into the crustal rocks of the ocean floor, which is then reprocessed in the energy zone.

As long as a natural balance exists between the gases in the air and the minerals available to the life system, the climate remains constant. The life system has a range of flexibility in its use of the gases and minerals and thus can maintain the cycling. Any major change in the balance or quantity of gases or minerals induces a climate change which restores a balance so the cycling can continue. The life system itself can expand or contract and even change genetically as required to maintain the cycling.

There are changes constantly taking place which upset the balance and the quantities of gases and minerals. An agricultural and technically competent society has the potential to control the balance of gases and minerals. We can do it if we can effect a major philosophical change in our attitude toward man and nature.

The abundance of living organisms on the land and in the water at any one time depends on the abundance of gases in the air and minerals available on the land and in the water. Microorganisms combine the gases and minerals to make the organic compounds from the microorganisms, and add the energy compounds of photosynthesis so that all the other life forms can have the life compounds and energy supplies to function.

The residues from all life processes on the land erode into the ocean. The microorganisms in the ocean use what they can—along with minerals in the ocean and gases in the air—to support the ocean chain of life. The various forms of ocean life convert the gases and minerals to solid substances which come to rest on the sea floor to form the sedimentary layers. The tectonic system completes the cycling of the elements.

The tectonic system is a hydraulic system. Its energy is derived from critical mass explosions in "hot spots" at about four hundred miles below the surface. The hot spots are columns of superheated melt in massive chimneys such as those in which the diamond mines of South Africa are located. The tops of the hot spots are incoming ocean floor. The face of the incoming ocean floor is melted off at a rate of a few centimeters per year. Above each "hot spot" are the tallest mountains. The mountains grow as the hot spots mature to full strength. The mountains take the full force of the explosions and disperse the hydraulic impact throughout the system, joined by the river of melt. Behind the hot spots is a section of ocean floor which is being or already has been raised to plateau status to become part of a continent. All of the hots spots in front of the plateau are called continental heaters.

Most of the superheated melt is recycled to the ridges in channels located in a hot zone two hundred miles below the surface. Some of the superheated melt moves upward through the sintered mass of high melting point compounds that constitute the earth's mantle. The melt oozing upward supplies heat and melt to the melted zone between the crust and the mantle. The ocean floor requires a large flow of melt to seal the innumerable cracks that occur when the floor is forced to flow to the heaters by the push from the ridges. The ridges alternately rise and fall due to fluctuations in pressure of the melt beneath them. This action results in a toggle effect which forces the two halves apart as melt rises in the crack between them. Flow to the continents is minimal because the continents are sealed against loss by old ocean floor slabs wedged under the edges of the continent. These are backed up by the sediments, eroded from the mantle, that probably contain unused radioactive components which separate by gravity to accumulate a critical mass. The explosions provide the energy to run the tectonic system. A small amount of sediments is fed into the hot spots with each movement of the sea floor into the heaters. Thus the mantle provides the continents with the molten rock to support a constantly increasing amount of land mass in proportion to sea floor. At some point the combination of use and decay of radioactive materials will not supply sufficient energy to meet the growing demand for energy. When that happens, the earth, like Mars, will become a dead planet.

With this knowledge of how the inanimate minerals and gases are cycled and recycled, we can understand the present climate changes.

The climate in the last half billion years has been predominantly hot, occasionally interrupted by short periods of glacial weather. The hot periods are characterized by hot steamy weather, copious rainfall, and jungle type vegetation in great abundance. Cataclysmic explosive events fill the atmosphere with greenhouse gases, dust from the ridge's crust, and dust from lava.

The explosions are caused when a continent splits apart or when a ridge is forced to move under a continent. The ridge, only two to five miles thick, stands above the ocean floor on a river of lava which feeds the crack between the two halves of the ridge. With the land side of the ridge held by the continent while hydraulic pressure under the ridge is fluctuating, it is inevitable that the ridge's plate will fail, and molten rock will flow out to meet cold sea water. The explosions that occur are similar to the volcanic island explosions of recent history which have occurred behind the Java continental heater. The explosions continue until the rate of flow in that area decreases enough to permit the water to freeze the opening. It is a weak seal; a rise in pressure plus ocean floor motion break the seal and start a new round of explosions. These sporadic explosions continue until the ridge is destroyed over a period of a million years.

Sometimes the explosions manage to penetrate to a heater. When that occurs, mountains are blown away, exposing hot spots to atmospheric pressure and influx of water. The contents of the hot spot chimney are then blown out by the nuclear explosive force. It is not surprising that such things as uranium and iridium are scattered over the western United States. Where the one hundred mile wide Gulf of California is located, there once were mountains connecting with the Sierra Nevada mountains and Western Sierra Madres of Mexico.

More often than not two or more catastrophic events occur at the same time. In the last sixty-five million years, the breakup of the old Pacific Ridge on the shores of the Americas occurred at about the same time as the explosive event offshore from India which resulted in an extensive lava flow. There may have been other catastrophic events. Such events require an expenditure of the melt between the crust and the mantle, causing the land masses and ocean floors to sink several hundred feet. Large areas of the land masses become shallow inland seas.

The breakup of Pangaea about two hundred twenty-five million years ago set off a string of catastrophic events, putting so much dust and greenhouse gases in the air that the lush growth spread to the upper latitudes. The heat and quantity of clouds were such that the precipitation fell as rain instead of snow. The ice was washed away and warm conditions existed above the Arctic Circle. The skull of a dinosaur was recently found there as well as the remains of a massive tree growth.

Catastrophic events eventually end. At the end of the Cretaceous Period, about sixty-seven million years ago, the dinosaurs began dying out. As the dust and gases were used up, food became scarce. Jungle growth changed to a more temperate growth, followed by desertification in the parts of the earth where solar energy accelerated the growth to use up the minerals. The dinosaurs moved north to find food. But the inevitable end of their daily food requirements came when the greenhouse gases dropped to the point where snow fell in the upper latitudes and winter killed the vegetation. Had the catastrophic events of sixty-five million years ago occurred a little earlier, the hot climate would have been renewed along with the minerals and gases to support sufficient microorganism growth to furnish life compounds for the dinosaurs.

The catastrophic events of the last two hundred twenty-five million years have run their course. The greenhouse gases can no longer sustain a hot climate. About three million years ago the polar ice accumulated. The approximately one hundred thousand year glacial cycle began. It takes ninety thousand years of glaciation to remineralize the world's soils and ten thousand years to demineralize the soils during the interglacial. We are at the end of the interglacial.

The microorganisms granulate the soil to aerate it for easy entrance of air and water. The depth of the aerated topsoil is the measure of the quantity and quality of the microorganisms and the life compounds they supply to the plant life. Our topsoils are now only inches deep. They ought to be measured in feet.

The entire world is suffering from malnutrition. Many species, both plant and animal, are dying out. Trees are starving to death. Others are burning in epidemic fashion; the thin topsoils cannot hold enough water during a few weeks of drought to supply enough moisture to make the trees fire resistant. People are dying from the diseases of malnutrition, because there is not enough daily supply of life compounds to support immune systems. Brains that do not function for lack of the life compounds result in a 25% illiteracy rate. The malnutrition is compounded by genetic corruption from the nonbiodegradable synthetic organic compounds and radioactive materials. Our children are saturated with these compounds and deprived nutritionally from conception. We elders put these stresses on our young people, and when they turn to alcohol and dope for momentary relief, all we can think of to do is tell people to "say no" and institute a "war on drug pushers." Is the adult brain and conscience so dead that we cannot deal with the basic problems? Are we so enslaved by the institution of greed destroying and contaminating the earth that we can only wait like animals for disease and famine to destroy us?

One way or another nature is going to keep on recycling the minerals and gases as long as there is enough energy released in the continental heaters to energize the system. The life on the land and in the water does not control the cycling. It is a part of the system. During the interglacial period, the residual mineral supply supports the life on the land. In the ocean the life is supported by runoff from the land plus the minerals ground in the polar regions and those released by the excavation of the ocean trenches in front of every heater. The combination of mineral supplies is sufficient to hold the gases in balance at an indicated 270 to 280 ppm CO_2. When the supply of minerals left by glaciation runs out, the life system can no longer hold in check the gases emitted by the tectonic system. The gases increase in the atmosphere, setting in motion the factors which cause glacial advance. We are watching it happen.

There is no such thing as a "warming." Those who predicted a warming did so in spite of the fact that the record shows that glaciation has in the past been initiated by a rise in CO_2. The CO_2 is a part of the glacial process. There is no evidence that those involved in the publicized climate study have any knowledge of the life system's role in maintaining the cycling of the gases and minerals or knowledge of how the tectonic system works. The life system is a matter for biologists—especially those who, since the mid 1970s, have studied such things as the interface between the root and the soil. The tectonic system is a thermomechanical system best understood by mechanical engineers. The life system has been ignored and geologists have been working on the tectonic system without checking their assumptions with engineers.

The recently issued preliminary draft EPA report to Congress on *Policy Options for Stabilizing Global Climate* is based on "the warming." It should have been based on the present and fast growing food crisis threatening the survival of civilization. The EPA is unaware of the fact that there is a crisis, otherwise they would not have offered the palliatives it proposes to send to the Congress.

Do we have a crisis?

1. Due to the lack of minerals in the soil, the soil organisms are dying out. Without them no other life can exist on earth. We are in a period of extinction or near extinction of all species of life. The thin topsoils and the low mineral content of foods testify to the disappearance of the soil organisms.

2. Every factor which raises the world albedo is now increasing at an accelerating rate. As a result, the permanent snow cover in the upper latitudes is steadily advancing toward the middle latitudes and growing seasons are shortening. Glaciation has begun.

3. The violence of weather caused by the cold air running into the warm air is taking a heavy toll on crop production. The violence can only accelerate as greenhouse gases increase and the glaciation continues.

4. The environment is saturated with nonbiodegradable synthetic organic compounds and radioactive nuclear contaminants. They kill or cause mutations in all living cells. Since they cannot be biologically degraded, they will be with us for a very long time. How much they will damage an effort to affect our survival no one can say.

5. At a time when all nations suffer from diseases of malnutrition and some from famine, none have reduced their population growth to zero or a negative rate. If the mind cannot overrule emotion, then we must watch each other die—and soon.

6. The world's economic laws have been established by the rich and for the rich. As a result, the "rich get richer and the poor get poorer." Eventually the dispossessed must revolt and demand a redistribution. Nations at war cannot carry on a survival program. All of the laws must be changed to bring the people of a nation together as a cohesive unit with the common objective of survival.

7. Finally there is the matter of the point of no return. It is conceivable that a massive survival effort could transfer most of

the greenhouse gases from the atmosphere to the soil, trees, and inland coastal waters in three or four decades. This would reduce the cloud cover and slow the rate of precipitation and hence the glacial advance. However, if the permanent snow cover is so large that the cold air descending over the land masses is sufficient to maintain the glacial circulation of air, the glaciation will continue. After the last glaciation, the CO_2 level stood at two hundred fifty ppm, thanks to the growth of microorganisms in generously remineralized soil and water. The tectonic activity was minimal after the glaciers stopped growing because the glaciers were melting in the middle latitudes from the effect of a hot sun in clear skies and from minimal snowfall. With very little greenhouse gas heating effect, the whole world of land and sea was cold. The temperature differential which has now initiated glaciation did not then exist. A few decades from now, the sea and the land will have cooled very little. If the permanent snow field maintains the glacial circulation of air, the lower latitudes will be dry and hot. Forests cannot grow on deserts. So we do not have the glaciation. What it boils down to is a race against the growing permanent snow cover.

Due to procrastination we find ourselves playing a game of Russian roulette in which the "six gun" is loaded with about three bullets instead of one.

These problems constitute a crisis. The leisurely pace proposed by the EPA study—typical of the views of the Congress and its scientists—is totally worthless as a response to the crisis. EPA does not understand the role of the soil and water microorganisms in the cycling of gases and minerals. They assume that stopping the use of fossil fuels, converting to other forms of energy, and planting forests is all it takes to stop the climate change. The truth is that trees will keep on dying and burning faster than we can plant new seedlings which will not grow on soils lacking in microorganisms. The gases now in the air must be removed and put into the only sinks available—topsoils, standing timber, and inland and coastal waters. Only the microorganisms can do the job. We must remineralize the soils and waters so the microorganisms can multiply. We must start the remineralization immediately, using whatever is available, until we can build an entire remineralization industry. The EPA preliminary report does not even mention this most basic of all actions which must be taken.

We are now living in a theory period that sees its salvation in an act of faith called annihilating the past. There is no system more certain to be wrong all the time than to abandon old values without first finding newer and better values. *Bread from Stones* told of a new and rational system for fertilization when it was first written. That system is still valid for reasons stated by Julius Hensel, reiterated by Albert Carter Savage, and driven to their ultimate conclusion by John D. Hamaker and Don Weaver.

Shortly before his untimely death at a young age, Larry Ephron handled *Acres U.S.A.* a very short paper styled *The Solution to Our Pesticide Problem.* In it he told about the German agricultural chemist, Julius Hensel, who discovered that by adding finely ground rock dust to soil he could confer immunity to bacterial, fungal and insect attack. In 1893 he put his ideas into a text, which is now the first entry in the *Acres U.S.A.* classics series.

> Since then [wrote Ephron] university scientists in several European countries have confirmed these findings and quantified them. Plants grown on soil well mineralized with rock dust grow much faster than plants grown with chemicals, need no chemical fertilizers or pesticides whatever, and produce yields on the order of 200 to 300% greater than on control plots. The best results are obtained with very finely ground dust from a mixture of many types of rocks, such as is found in glacial or river gravel, which contains the full spectrum of minerals. The inexpensiveness of gravel dust compared to chemicals will enable many family farms to stay in business.
>
> The crops grown on such soil seem to be much hardier, more likely to survive climatic extremes such as heat, cold, and drought. That alone seems sufficient reason to remineralize our farmlands quickly, with the climate already worsening from the rapidly increasing greenhouse effect. Any surpluses can replenish our dwindling reserves, and be stockpiled by government against expected climatic disasters. Food grown on remineralized soil has been found to contain substantially more nutrients than chemically grown food (almost 50% more calcium, 80% more potassium in one study) so those of us who eat it should be hardier as well.

Moreover, wrote Ephron, studies show rock dust also produces a comparable effect on trees–greatly increased resistance to insects, disease and climatic extremes, and much faster growth. Massive tree planting has been proposed as the one thing we can do to actually reduce the greenhouse effect rather than simply slowing its rise, since trees consume one of the most prevalent greenhouse gases, carbon dioxide. By remineralizing the soil of newly planted forests as well as existing ones, we can magnify the effectiveness of these efforts several-fold, gaining some crucial time to phase in a less polluting way of life.

Larry Ephron was Director of People for a Future in Berkeley, California. His films and writings made him both a lineal descendent of Hensel and a progenitor of a new breed of scientists who will lead American agriculture into Century 21. The reader can join the latter select group by reading carefully, and by taking on this classical work with a highlighter pen in hand.—*Charles Walters Jr.*

FROM THE ORIGINAL PUBLISHER

This somewhat informal little book, translated from the writings of Julius Hensel, and other German writers, is designed to introduce to the people of the United States a subject that is of vital importance to everyone, young and old. It is a subject in which all should take an interest, even if it be but a selfish one, for it concerns the *health* of the human race. Ten years ago [in 1883] Hensel, a thinker and a chemist, tentatively put forth his little work, *The Makrobiotic*, and, later, a larger work, *Das Leben*. At first these attracted but little attention, but gradually an increasing number of readers sought those original books and new editions of both were called for. Each work was revised, largely rewritten and published in German by the publishing house of Boericke & Tafel, Philadelphia, Pennsylvania, and at the same time the former was translated into English and published. As the titles show the subjected treated is a large one—*Das Leben*, or Englished, *The Life*. The part of the subject that bears on agriculture is the topic of this book. At first was but theory; but during the past few years the factory has passed into the domain of verified science, not, however, without meeting with much fierce opposition—the same opposition that has greeted every great new truth on its advent.

For years mankind has tacitly accepted the idea that fertilizing must be done, in plain Anglo-Saxon, with filth—animal, bird or human excrement, rotten bones, sewage, rotten anything, reinforced, to be sure, with such chemical matter as nitre, super-phosphates, lime, etc. Yet every one knows that, despite all such matter put on the earth, the land is slowly but surely losing its fertility; that insect pests increase, and, what is not so well known, the *quality* of the earth's products is deteriorating. Hensel saw what some day all the world will see, that plants require healthy food in order to flourish as much as man or beast does, and that sewage, etc., was *not* a healthy food.

As will be seen in the following pages, he goes back to the beginning in his search for plant food and finds it in the primeval rocks. Fed on such foods, plants will yield to mankind cereals, tubers and fruits that are healthy, wholesome and life-sustaining; the plants being healthy will escape disease and parasites, and many of the ills of man due to unwholesome food from plants will disappear. Is it not sound reason to believe that food-yielding plants grown on pure, uncontaminated soil will be wholesomer than those grown on soil saturated with sewage and rotting manure from stables?

This is but a brief outline of the theories propounded by Hensel and put in practice in Germany for the last five or six years with amazing success. Put in practice in this country it will not only free the farmer from a heavy yearly expense for artificial fertilizers but will gradually bring back his exhausted fields to their virgin state and give the public food on which health may be maintained. In Germany this has become a "cause" sustained by enthusiastic supporters not only among farmers, horticulturalists, florists and gardners, but also among clergymen, physcians and public-spirited men. They see in it one of the means by which the human race is to be at least physically regenerated, and a sound body is a proper base for a sound mind.

PREFACE

What will fertilizing with stone dust accomplish?
It will:
1. Turn stones into bread and make barren regions fruitful.
2. Feed the hungry.
3. Cause healthy cereals and provender to be harvested and thus prevent epidemics among men and diseases among animals.
4. Make agriculture again profitable and save great sums of money which are now expended either for fertilizers that in part are injurious and in part useless.
5. Turn the unemployed to country life by revealing the inexhaustible nutritive forces which, hitherto unrecognized, are stored up in the rocks, the air and the water.
This it will accomplish.
May this little book be intelligible enough that men, who seem on the point of becoming beasts of prey, may cease their war of all against all and instead unite in the common conquest of the

stones. May mankind, instead of hunting for gold, facing for fame, or wasting productive forces in useless labors, choose the better part: The peaceable emulation in the discovery and direction of the natural forces for evolving nutritive products and the peaceable enjoyment of the fruits which the earth is able to produce in abundance for all. May man use his divine heritage of reason to attain true happiness by discovering the sources whence all earthly blessings flow and thus put an end to self-seeking and greed, to the increasing difficulties of making a living, the anxieties for the daily bread, to distress and crime—such is the aim of this little work, and in this may God aid us!

Hermsdorf below Kynast, October 1st, 1893.

1

THE CAUSE OF THE DECADENCE
OF AGRICULTURE

The yield of the ground is steadily decreasing. Everywhere is distress. Our fields do not yield sufficiently abundant crops to compete with the cheap lands of the far West. To change this condition is the object of this book.

It is now 400 years since the second half of the world was discovered, but the whole earth is only now discovered, so far as the knowledge is concerned, of how the inexhaustible treasures may be utilized which are at our disposal in the nourishing forces of the rocks of the mountains. Instead of working this colossal mine men have bought the material for restoring the fertility of the exhausted soil in the form of medicine, i.e., chemical fertilizers.

For the last fifty years a dogma has crept into agriculture which calls itself *The Law of Minimum*, namely:

"That one of the substances which the plant requires and which is contained in the minimum quantity in your fields you must furnish to it in the form of a fertilizer."

This false precept owes its reception solely to the defective method of chemical investigation which prevailed fifty years ago.

As there was found a considerable quantity of phosphoric acid and of potash in the ashes of all seeds, and as these do not exist in the air and must therefore be furnished by the soil, it was very natural that the inquiry was started, how much of these substances necessary for the raising of plants is still at hand in the soil?

While the soil was then investigated and was treated with *muriatic acid*, in order that the substances contained might be dissolved, there were found only inconsiderable quantities of potash and of phosphoric acid in this solution, because the alkalies in the soil which are combined with silicic acid are as little dissolved by muriatic acid as, *e.g.,* powdered glass. In order to be able to define the amount of potash, it is necessary first to drive out the silicic acid by the use of fluoric acid after having converted it into volatile fluoride of silicium; this method was not used by the former agricultural chemists. As in consequence thereof they overlooked the presence of potash, so also did they fail to notice the phosphoric acid which is combined with alumina and iron in the silicates, because when the iron was precipitated from the solution the whole of the alumina and phosphoric acid was precipitated with it; the further examination of the fluid solution therefore gave a negative result with respect to phosphoric acid and this is also the case at this day if we work according to the old method.

The teachers of agriculture therefore announced:

"Of potash and of phosphoric acid, these most important nutriments of plants, there is only a *minimum* left in the soil; therefore, we must first of all supply potash and phosphoric acid to our fields."

To these two substances *nitrogen* was also added. Nitrogen in the form of vegetable albumen is on the average contained in such quantities in plants that its weight frequently exceeds that of the fixed constituents of the ashes. The following may serve to explain this. The affinity of the earthy substances (lime, magnesia and oxide of iron) and of the fixed alkalies with respect to hydrocarbons, as may be seen in the soaps, which consist of combinations of potassa or soda with oleic acid ($C_{18}H_{34}O_2$) or with stearic acid ($C_{18}H_{36}O_2$). Of like affinity with these earths and the fixed alkalies is the volatile alkali Ammonia N.H.H.H. This explains why when there are not sufficient earths carried up in the juice to complete the upbuilding of plants in their stalks and leaves their place is filled by ammonia, which, as before said, is formed from the nitrogen and the watery vapor of the air. The wood in the trunk of trees contains no nitrogen at all, but the leaves of trees contain a quantity of nitrogen; the parenchyma of the leaves condenses it from the air because the sphere of actions of the earths, which extends even unto the veins of the leaves, does not reach the parenchyma.

Now, in view of the great quantity of nitrogen found in the produce of the fields and of which agriculturists presuppose that it is derived through the roots of plants from the earth, they came to the same result as with respect to potash and phosphoric acid; i.e., they found only a vanishing *"minimum"* of it in the soil, and therefore they concluded: "Our crops have already consumed all the potash, all the phosphoric acid, and all the nitrogen; these substances are, therefore, in *minimum* proportions in the soil. If we are not to miserably starve we must bring this minimum in abundance into our fields in the form of manures."

The result is that the use of Super-Phosphates, *Sulfate* of *Ammonia, Guano* and *Chili-nitre* has enormously increased, but agriculture has entered into the sign of the cancer (retrogression), for it may easily be seen that if the cost of fertilizers amounts to more than the harvest the farmers must emigrate.

It took a long while before the teachers of agriculture economy, having the fact pointed out to them by practical farmers who judged with clear eyes and sound reason that crops of peas and beans rich in nitrogen prosper on soil entirely void of nitrogen, at least granted that leguminous plants derive their whole supply of nitrogen exclusively from the air, which as to full four-fifth consists of nitrogen. It is difficult for them to admit that other plants also do this, because their reputation and their income is mainly derived from the theory of potash, nitrogen and phosphoric acid. They explain this by asserting:

"There are *producers* of nitrogen and there are *consumers* of nitrogen."

It is of course true that plants also assimilate such nitrogen as their roots find in the soil, but that is by no means necessary. The forest trees furnish us with a most convincing proof of this. Birches, beeches and oaks grow to gigantic size on bare rocks of granite and porphyry. To be convinced of this, let anyone ascend the Herd mountains! Now as beech leaves and oak leaves contain one full percent of their weight of nitrogen, while beech wood and oak wood are devoid of nitrogen, the nitrogen of the leaves has evidently been furnished, not by the rock, but by the air.

It is manifest that if the soil were the proper source of nitrogen, the roots being in immediate contact with the soil ought to show at least as much nitrogen as the parts above ground which are surrounded with air; but, on the contrary, they contain less.

For example, one pound of potatoes contains about 25 grains of nitrogen, but the green potato stems and leaves contain more than 42 grains to the pound, and it is from the plant that the tubers draw their nitrogen and not the reverse; for the potato herb, which in the beginning was so exuberant in juice, about the time the tubers mature becomes thin, hollow and light, because the juice containing the nitrogen descends into the tubers. So also does one pound of the green plant of the carrot contain about 35 grains of nitrogen, but the carrot-roots contain only about 14 grains to the pound.

We may also mention that just as the nitrogen descends into tubers it also passes up into the seeds, so that cereals show as much as 140 grains of nitrogen to the pound. The green stalk of grains show a similar proportion of nitrogen, while in a pound of straw there are only found 33 to 49 grains of nitrogen.

That the chemical fertilizers that are still all the fashion are a mere *waste* may be mathematically demonstrated by taking any example at random. I will choose for this the *sugar-beets* and the *carrot.*

The sugar-beet according to Wolff's tables shows the following ashes per kilogram (2 1-10 lbs.):

Potash 3.8	Phosphoric acid 0.9
Soda 0.6	Sulfuric acid 0.2
Lime 0.4	Silicic acid 0.2
Magnesia 0.6	Muriatic acid 0.3

According to atomic equivalents this would make 142 for phosphoric acid, 80 for sulfuric acid, 60 for silicic acid, 73 for muriatic acid, 90 for potash, 62 for soda, 56 for lime and 40 for magnesia. Now the above:

    0.9 of phosphoric acid would saturate 0.6 potash.

    0.3 of sulfuric acid would saturate 0.35 potash.

    0.2 of silicic acid would saturate 0.3 potash.

    0.3 of muriatic acid would saturate 0.4 potash.

Thus all the acid together would saturate 1.65 potash.

There remains, therefore, the following excess of bases:

Potash 2.15
Soda 0.6
Lime 0.4
Magnesia 0.6

Or if we count the 0.6 of soda, 0.4 of lime and 0.6 of magnesia equivalent with 1.65 of potash, then the entire quantity of potassa in the sugar-beet, amounting to 3.85, would be at our disposal. This potassa we may consider as combined with sugar, cellular tissue and albumen. Beside these 3.8 potassa, 1.6 of nitrogen, or, in round numbers, 1.9 of ammonia, is to be taken into account as being also an unsaturated basic constituent of the beet-root. From this it proximately follows: That the 3.8 potassa cannot result from the manuring with sulfate of potassa, for else it would need the presence of 3.25 of sulfuric acid, while there is only 0.3 present, nor can the 1.9 of ammonia be due to the sulfate of ammonia, else they would call for 5.0 instead of only 0.3. If, therefore, we manure sugar-beets with sulfate of potassa and sulfate of ammonia these substances are to be regarded, as already stated, as largely wasted. As the source of the potash and the soda for the sugar-beets we can only consider the feldspar, which, thanks to God, is still contained to a certain degree in the soil, while the nitrogen is furnished by the atmosphere.

The feldspar in the soil will in the end of course become exhausted, and must then be supplied by manuring with the rock fertilizer.

A computation shows that to supply 0.3 sulfuric acid 0.6 gypsum which is combined with water will suffice; thus if the acre of land is to furnish two hundredweight of beets it would need, among other things, only 13 1/4 pounds of gypsum.

As a parallel we will now consider the carrot. The ashy constituents for one kilogram (2,206 pounds) are, according to Wolff's tables, as follows:

Potash	. . . . . .3.0	Phosphoric acid	. . . . .1.1
Soda	. . . . .1.7	Sulfuric acid	. . . . . . .0.5
Lime	. . . . . . .0.9	Silicic acid	. . . . .0.2
Magnesia	. . . .0.4	Muriatic acid	. . . . . . .0.4

A comparison with the sugar-beet roots shows that the carrot contains somewhat less potash and magnesia but somewhat more soda and lime; besides this, the carrot contains about one-third more of phosphoric, sulfuric acid and muriatic acid. These variations seem to be caused by manuring with liquid stable manure; as to the rest we recognize that for the basic constituents of potassa, soda, lime and magnesia in the carrots the pulverized primary rocks of the soil are the natural sources.

We find that all plants, as also all animal bodies (for these are built up from vegetable substances), after combustion, leave behind ashes which always consist of the same substances, although the proportions of admixture vary with the different kinds of plants. We always find in these ashes potash, soda, lime, magnesia, iron and manganese combined with carbonic, phosphoric, sulfuric, muriatic, fluoric and silicic acids. These ashy constituents give their form and connection to the bodies of plants and animals according to the manner indicated above.

Now, inasmuch as the plants spring from the soil, it is manifest that the enumerated earthy or ashy constituents must be furnished by the soil. And, as in the soil these substances are present in combination with silica and alumina, the origin of the soil thence becomes manifest. It has arisen from the disintegrated primary rocks, all of which contain more or less potassa, soda, lime, magnesia, manganese and iron, besides phosphoric, sulfuric, chlorine, fluorine, silica and alumina. From such earthy material from primary rocks, which have been associated with sediments of gypsum and lime, in combination with water and the atmosphere under the influence of the warmth and light of the sun, the plants which nourish man and beast originate.

Now, as all the enumerated earthy materials with the exception of silica and alumina enter into the crops that are taken away from field, it is clear that they must be replaced. If we desire normal and healthy crops, and that men and animals living on them should find in them all that is necessary for their bodily sustenance (phosphate and fluorate of lime and magnesia for the formation of the bones and teeth, potassa, iron and manganese for the muscles, chloride of sodium for the serum of the blood, sulfur for the albumen of the blood, hydrocarbons for the nerve-fat), it will not suffice to merely restore the potassa, phosphoric acid and nitrogen. Other things are imperatively demanded.

With regard to this I shall adduce one instructive example: The proprietor of an extensive estate wrote to me that he formerly manured with ammonia, super-phosphate and Chili-nitre, and although there was a steady retrogression in the yields, yet he continued to earn something. Of late, however, when he had passed over to manuring with iron slag and Chili-nitre, with a steady retrogression, at last neither rye, nor barley, nor oats would prosper, only, strange to say, wheat gave a tolerable yield. How could I explain this to him? To this question I gave the desired answer by pointed to the *ashy constituents*. The ashes of barley and oats contain five times as much sulfuric acid as wheat. The latter could still find its small requisite of sulfuric acid in the soil, but for oats, barley and rye these feeble remains did not suffice.

Now as we have seen that the primary rocks in the mountain ranges, porphyry, granite and gneiss, through the mellowing and crumbling influence of thousands of years (for nothing else is meant by "disintegration"), has produced the fertile soil which furnishes us with healthy nourishing plants, it may easily be seen that when such a soil has been almost exhausted of the elements that nourish plants through a cultivation of several hundred of years and a yearly turning over with the plough or the spade, the original natural strength cannot be restored to it by means of medicines and single chemicals, but this can only be effected by supplying new soil out of which nothing has grown, and the strength of which is therefore intact.

To gain such new soil we need not wait a thousand years till wintry cold, snow and rain crumble the rocky material and bring it down into the valleys. We have only to put our hands to work, and from the proper rocks obtain the necessary materials to rejuvenate the old and wornout soil and restore it again to virgin fertility.

2

HEALTHY AND UNHEALTHY PRODUCE

According to the chemical examination of the ashes which remain when plants are incinerated, the average result shows about as much potash and soda as lime and magnesia. Silicic acid is somewhat more than one-fifth of the sum of these four bases, chlorine about one-twentieth of the whole, phosphoric acid is one-sixth, but sulfuric acid is only one-fourth in weight of the phosphoric acid.

Granite rocks contain an average of 6% of potassa and soda, while their contents of phosphoric acid are more than 1%, granite by itself will readily fulfill the demands for vegetable growth, as may be confirmed by a report in the papers received while writing this. We read:

"In Deutmansdorf, Kreis Loewenberg, in Silesia, were found on the heap of refuse from the quarries three stalks of rye with ears containing 90 to 100 grains." (*General Anzeiger fur Schlesien and Posen*, October 1, 1893.)

As to chlorine, this mostly reaches our cultivated plants through manuring with liquid manure containing salt, and has been proved directly injurious to the growth and quality of many plants. In this respect it is sufficient to point to the evil effects of manuring tobacco with liquid manure. Chlorine is not found in wheat, rye, barley and oats, millet and buckwheat, linseed, apples and pears, plums and gooseberries, acorns and chestnuts, nor in the wood of any forest trees. We need, therefore, not consider chlorine in fertilizing our fields.

Now, when I state that the given proportions of the ashes have yielded this average in comparing more than 80 analyses of the ashes of the various parts of plants, it need not be concluded from this that any particular plant, or the particular part of a plant, needs a quite definite proportion of ashy constituents, but it is found on the contrary that the earthy constituents of the same kind of plants differ in various ways. This explains why we find the same species of plants to flourish now on calcareous soil, now on soil formed from granite, gneiss or porphyry as an example of which I shall only mention sheep's-yarrow, *Achillea millefolium*. This is effected in great part by the fact that potassa and soda are interchangeable, but these two alkalis may also be replaced in most plants to a considerable part by the alkaline earths, lime and magnesia; but, of course, the nutritive value of the plants and the other qualities cannot then remain the same. Potassa and soda may even be *wholly* lacking in a plant and they may be *entirely* replaced by lime and magnesia. As this fact is not as yet found in any book, I cannot refuse a challenge as to proof. I name as my witnesses the royal mason, *Wimmel*, of Berlin, and engineer *Klug*, of Landshut. In company with these gentlemen I visited, on June 25th, of this year (1893), the loftily situated marble quarry near Rothenzechau. In the neighborhood of this marble quarry the vegetation is always somewhat behind in time to that of the valley, by the end of May, they have passed away. We found such dandelions there growing immediately on the marble rock, where this had water flowing over it, and the flowerstalks reached the height of about a foot and a half. There was not, indeed, any great wealth of leaves, and the thick and high flowerstalks themselves could be broken like glass into pieces, which I did not weary in repeating before the eyes of my companions. Now this Silesian marble is a very white dolomite, consisting, therefore, of carbonate of lime and carbonate of magnesia; but it must also surely contain besides this some phosphate and sulfate of lime besides a trace of carbonate of protoxide of iron, the presence of which is demonstrated in the moist clefts of the marble by a brown oxidation. These plants, therefore, grew on a sub-stratum of almost pure lime and magnesia. This extreme example convinces us that the alkaline earths (lime and magnesia) may really replace the alkalis (potassa and soda) in the building up of plants, and this also furnishes us with the explanation why the iron-slag, as a preeminently calcareous fertilizer, unmistakably caused an increase of crops on fields which were deficient in lime. The same result might, indeed, have been reached more cheaply by directly spreading the lime on them. But there is another "But" in this matter, for in harvests it is not merely the quantity, but much more the quality which has to be considered.

Even if the striking example cited makes it manifest that lime may in great part replace the alkalis in building up plants, giving to them the same *form*, and, indeed, making them of imposing size, nevertheless the *quality* and the *internal worth* of the products of the soil is considerably influenced by the difference in its basic constituents. I, therefore, mentioned, not unintentionally, that the flower stalks of the dandelion grown on marble could be broken like glass into separate pieces, while on the contrary dandelion stalks growing on soil containing *potassa* may be bent into rings and formed into chains, as is frequently done by children. Potassa makes pliable and soft, lime makes hard and brittle. Flax is a very good example of this.

Silesian linen made of the flax growing on our granite soil rich in potassa is celebrated for its suppleness, softness and durability, while the Spanish and French linen produced on calcareous soils is hard, of little strength of fibre and of small value. What avails it then that the Spanish flax exceeds the Silesian by twice its length?

As with textile plants so with plants serving for nourishment and for fodder. It is manifest that where calcareous plants have not the same nutritive value as those in which alkalis and earth are harmoniously associated that the former are not as healthy as the latter. With reference to this, Dr. Stamm, who practiced in Zurich (where, in 1884, I saw a whole mountain of lime dug away), states that he nowhere saw so many examples of ossification of the arteries as on the Swiss soil so rich in lime; the fact that the drinking water is correspondingly rich in lime may contribute to it. The strong, bony frame of the Swiss strikes every one, even those travelers who visit Switzerland only for a short trip. This was an essential reason why Winkelried in 1386 at Sempach could with his strong boned arms hold a whole dozen of lances of the knights, and 1,400 Swiss could win the victory over 6,000 Austrians who were fed on meat, wine and flour, and this despite of their 4,000 horsemen in armor.

How much influence nutrition exercises on temperament and breed may be seen from the breeders of fine horses. As Prof. Marossy communicated to me, Englishmen import the oats for their race horses from Hungary. Why? Because the granite of the Carpathian mountains is rich in potassa but contains but little lime. Potassa makes supple, but lime makes tough and awkward. The counterpart of the world-renowned Hungarian saddle horses and carriage horses is found in the strong-boned Norman breed horse which derives its peculiarities from the French chalky soil, and could not be easily replaced as draught animals before the heavy stone wagons, the baggage wagons and the brewers' wagons with their heavy loads of beer barrels.

And is it possible that the human race should be uninfluenced by its nutrition? Let us make some comparisons: Wine contains almost only phosphate of potassa, for the calcareous ingredients are precipitated during the fermentation as tartar. Hence the French *esprit*, the Austrian good nature, the artistic inspiration of the wine-drinking Italians. but like a stone wall in the battle stand the Pommeranian potato-eating grenadiers. In the ashes remaining from potatoes we find the following proportions: 44 potassa, 4 soda, 64 lime, 33 magnesia, 16 phosphoric acid and 13 sulfuric acid. Sulfur is indispensable in the formation of normal bile and of tendons. Also hair and wool require much sulfur, about 5% of their weight.

After some such hints as to nutrition it cannot be indifferent what kind of crops we raise for our nourishment and with what substances our fields are fertilized. It cannot be all sufficient that great quantities are harvested, but the great quantity must also be of *good quality*. It is undisputable that by merely fertilizing with marl; i.e., with carbonate of lime, such a large yield may be gained as to make a man inclined to always content himself with marl, but with such a one-sided fertilization slowly but surely evil effects of various kinds will develop; these have given rise to the axiom of experience: "Manuring with lime makes rich fathers but poor sons."

Despite such experience, however, after a certain time, when those who experienced the damage have passed away, manuring with lime always again becomes a fashion. So even now. The harvests after manuring with lime are so favorable that there are those who expect their salvation from fertilizing with lime. Not long ago the German Agricultural Society granted a prize to a paper on "Fertilizing with Lime." But such prizes do not prove anything. Also a paper on Chili-nitre as a fertilizer received a prize. But how has this substance, so poisonous for plants and animals, fallen into disgrace!

Lime, indeed, is not directly injurious to plant growth, on the contrary it is useful and necessary, but everything has its measure and its limits. Lime can only produce wholesome cereals, vegetables and forage when there is at the same time a sufficiency of potassa and soda.

"Too much of a thing is good for nothing!" In this connection I have to add a few things more. In the same way as lime and magnesia can replace potassa and soda in the structure of plants so all these four constituents can in great part be replaced by basic *Ammonia*, without any resultant appreciable change in the *form* of the plants, except that this appears strikingly luxuriant and *rich in leaves*, as the milfoil on and near the mounds of cemeteries.

Such a substitution of ammonia for the alkalis and the alkaline earths correspond in some degree to the relation between potassa-alum and ammonia-alum, which are so similar in form that they cannot be distinguished without a chemical examination. In an analogous manner the muriate of ammonia has quite a similar taste to the muriate of soda, and the sulfate of ammonia almost the same bitter taste as sulfate of soda (Glauber's salt) and sulfate of magnesia (Epsom salts), but the *effects* of these salts vary considerably.

A particularly interesting example of the fact that the appearance of plants in which ammonia has largely taken the place of the fixed alkalis and earths is found in *tobacco leaves*. Only specialists can at once recognize their quality at a glance; the great majority only perceive the difference when the leaves, made into cigars, are lighted. Then the one kind, grown on the Virginia soil, rich in magnesia and lime, gives us light, loose ashes and a fine aroma, while the product of Vierraden (Prussia), manured with stable dung and liquid manure, in which ammonia takes the place of lime and magnesia, "coals," and diffuses an unpleasant odor. It is quite similar with plants raised for nourishment or for fodder. The inability of offering resistance, as seen in the "lodging" of grain after manuring with dung and liquid manure, after a long rain, and, in accordance with this, the grain also which is harvested from such a field has no firmness; it becomes soft in grinding, smearing the mill-stones, so that no grain raised with stable manure can be ground without mixing it with Western or California grain, and it has always a lesser value. So the barley raised with stable manure produces a malt which the brewer refuses to buy, as it would spoil his beer.

Now, as these ammoniacal plants lack the internal firmness and the ability of offering resistance, so also they cannot be healthy for animals when used as fodder, for the animal bodies have no consistence without *earths*. But these earths are subject to elimination owing to respiration. The ashy constituents of the blood-disks, which are oxidized by respiration; i.e., sulfate and phosphate of lime, magnesia and iron, are eliminated from the organism with the secretion of the kidneys, as also the bases present in the flesh of the muscles; i.e., potassa and soda; for the muscular substance also is oxidized through the oxygen of the arterial blood.

Now, as the earthy or ashy constituents, which are specifically necessary for the albumen of the blood, as well as for the flesh of the muscles and for the renewal of the bones (for *all* parts of the body are subject to this mutation of substance), are not replaced by the substances in the fodder, it is an unavoidable sequence that a relaxation and loosening of the tissues, brittleness of the bones and every kind of disturbance of health should take place without cattle. I shall only adduce one single very instructive example in proof of this out of my neighborhood.

The hotel keeper in Carlsthal, near Schreiberhau, in the Riesengebirge, kept twelve beeves. The manure from the cattle he conveyed to a swampy meadow, which up to that time had only produced sour grasses; but after the stable manure was applied it yielded so luxurious a growth of grass that he used the abundance to feed his twelve oxen and cows. It was not long, however, before the cattle became decrepit and ten of them died. The cause of this was the fodder grown from stable manure, in which ammonia supplied the place of the fixed alkalis, potassa, soda, lime and magnesia. The other two beeves were quickly sold, for they suffered from lickerishness; i.e., they refused their food and gnawed instead the cribs and other wood in the stable. For all wood contains about 3% of earthy substance, and the cattle craved these earthy substances in order to gain firm flesh and bones. The two oxen recovered when their new owner gave them a different fodder.

This same reason serves to explain other cases lately observed. It has been found that some kinds of pork do not bear pickling. While salt and nitrate of potash insure the keeping of pickled meat, the meat of certain hogs when lying in brine very soon passes into putrefaction, but into a decomposition different from the usual kind. The process that takes place is like what is called the "cheesy degeneration," which chemically means that the connective and muscular tissues decompose into peptones (Leucin and Tyrosin) as during digestion.

To explain this phenomenon we must consider the cheesy degeneration of the lung-tissue in consumptives. In their blood there is also always a deficit in lime and sulfur, which are absolutely necessary in the formation of red blood-disks.

Now, on inquiring why this pork when pickled underwent such a peculiar change, it was found that the animals had been fattened with Fray Bentos Meat Powder. But the lean meat contains as its chief ashy constituent only phosphate of potassa with almost imperceptible traces of lime and sulfur. Lime, indeed, is not found in the meat but in the bones, which are devoured by the tiger and the dog, but not by man. Therefore we have to gain the calcareous supply for our blood, our bones and our teeth from calcareous corn and from vegetables rich in lime. As our present fine flour, freed from bran, is furnished us almost devoid of sulfur and lime we need not wonder at the great number of modern maladies.

Now when hogs are fed with Fray Bentos Meat Powder, devoid of lime, in place of vegetable food, rich in lime, they cannot acquire a strong bony frame, and in consequence we need not wonder at the flaccidity, sponginess and easy putrefaction of the meat of such animals. If they had not been slaughtered in good time these helpless animals likely would have succumbed to some hog disease.

From this we may draw our conclusions with respect to human health. Many a one considers a meat diet to be a godsend, but is plagued on that account with rheumatism asthma and corpulency, to cure which he is ordered to drink some mineral waters which contain lime, magnesia and sulfate of soda.

To return to agriculture and the feeding of cattle. Nitrogenous foods are supposed to be strength givers; this is a theoretic error full of fatal consequences for agriculture. We never have had as many cattle plagues as we have had since artificial fertilizer and "strong" foods have been in vogue.

The theorists in nutrition who demand that man should have so much of hydrocarbon, so much fat and so much albumen have evidently little conception of the close relationship in which these substances stand to one another, by which the one may pass over into the other; e.g., the hydrocarbon *sugar* through the adjunction of earths and ammonia becomes albumen. But albumen easily undergoes a change into fat, as may be seen in cheese, and also from the manner in which the meat of the ham passes into fat. The same transformation takes place in nutriments containing hydrocarbons; e.g., the malt sugar of beer drinkers and the starch of grasses. Many an ox accumulates a few hundred points of tallow and yet is not fed with fat or butter, but with grass, hay and grain.

The so-called "strong" food of cattle, therefore, amounts to nothing and ought rather to be called poison-food. The truly strong food for cattle consists of mountain herbs, rich in earth, when these besides alkalis also contain lime and magnesia. Just think of the dairy cows of the Swiss Alps and of the cattle in Holstein that derive their strength from the grass of the marshes which are not fertilized with stable manure, but which are preserved in their lasting fertility by the neighboring rocky highlands, which continually enables the rain to wash down the soluble rocky material which enriches the meadows.

As a counterpart to the pork raised from Fray Bentos Meat Flour I will mention here an example from my own observation. Here (on the Kynast) I kept two sheep. I once saw them eating lime from the wall of the stable, as chickens do when they need lime for their egg-shells. From this I concluded that the grasses growing on my soil, in which there is little lime, did not supply them with sufficient sustenance for their bones. I, therefore, mixed some whiting with their cooked roots and this craving for lime ceased. When I at last sold the animals to the butcher he was so pleased at their solid meat that he desired to bespeak immediately some sheep for the next year.

I would here mention that the sheep-raiser, Mr. von Wiedebach, in Guben, inquired of me whether the principles of my *Makrobiotik* were not applicable to cattle-raising, especially so as to put an end to the mortality among sheep and to the mouth-disease and the foot-rot; I advised him to give in certain proportion precipitated chalk or whiting, flowers of sulfur and copperas, as a periodical addition to their food; and he has repeatedly assured me that by these means he has in very many places, whither he has been called as a specialist, put an end to the mortality of the cattle, and has brought them in other places to a normal state of health.

Chemistry teaches us that the characteristic nature of the albumen rich in ammonia consists in the easy interchangeableness of their atomic groups; but just on this account muscular fibre and connective tissue can be built up from the albumen of the blood, but every case has two sides. The ease with which the constituents of albumen can be shifted also favors their chemical decomposition. Need I mention here the savory taste of fresh-laid eggs and the smell of rotten ones? Intelligent people have long since perceived that feeding with albumen does not do all that the theorists claim. It does not pay for its expenses.

The chemical "strong" food for the *soil* in shape of the Chilinitre, which contains nitrogen, and has been awarded the premium over all its competitors, has proved a miserable failure; but the theorists are indefatigable. They now advocate chemical "strong" food for *cattle*, and there are many people who put this latest theory into disastrous practice.

All of us have to bear the evil consequences of this. Does not stable-feeding cohere with this "strong" feeding and this forced fattening? And does not the stable air so poor in oxygen cause the murrain of cattle? And does not the mortality of our children spring from the cow-milk poor in earths? That in consequence of fertilizing with stable manure crops poor in earths are produced is indubitable after what has been stated above. From these nutriments poor in earths again follows a host of ills—nervous debility, nervous sufferings, decomposition of lymph and serum, which are continually becoming more prevalent. Among these diseases are anaemia, chlorosis, scrofula, swelling of the lymphatic glands, cutaneous diseases, asthma, catarrhal states, nervousness, epilepsy, gout, rheumatism, corpulency, dropsy, consumption, diabetes, etc., as I have demonstrated anatomically and physiologically in a manner easily comprehended in the book *Makrobiotik* or *Our Diseases and Our Remedies*. Fertilizing with stone-meal will in future give us normal and healthy crops and fodder.

3

WHAT SHALL WE DO
WITH STABLE MANURE?

So long as attention was not called to the fact that new earth from pulverized primitive rock, together with the carbonate and sulfate of lime, forms the best and most natural fertilizer for an exhausted soil, men directed their attention to that part of the food which cattle do not assimilate, but excrete, for manure. So men came pretty generally to the position that we must bring dung to an exhausted field, else nothing can grow. Now in order to get manure we must raise cattle; for these stables and attendants are necessary, and a considerable area of land must be devoted to provide the necessary fodder. Now since it is said that without manure nothing can grow, manure must be used to make fodder grow on which cattle feed in order to produce manure for more fodder. In such a circle of life where does the advantage of keeping cattle come in? The raising of cattle only pays in mountainous regions, where the fructifying dew transforms the stones into herbs, or in the marshes irrigated by canals, for here the subsoil is naturally moist, and without water nothing can grow. In marshy regions the raiser of cattle can put his hands in his pockets and look on while the ox "eats money into his pocket;" but elsewhere the ox rather eats money out of the owner's pockets than into them.

But anyways the production of milk, cheese and wool, as well as the necessity of having horses for driving, makes the raising of cattle and horses a factor that must be taken into consideration.

Now as all cattle produce manure, solid and liquid, the question arises: "What shall we do with it?"

The fact that stable manure undoubtedly promotes the growth of plants gives to it a certain value. This value does not depend upon the nitrogen but on earthy or ashy constituents which it contains, and on the combinations of hydrocarbons; i.e., these carbonate carbohydrates do not need to be first produced by the sun, but may be utilized by a simple change of grouping and may be compared to ready-made building stone that may at once be built into the plants with this result that their growth may take place in the cool springtime *more quickly* than where the warm sun must do the whole work of drawing the carbon out of the carbonate rocks in conjunction with water. Still this advantage will no more be considered so decisive because the same result, yea, a result almost four times as great according to my experience, may be attained by a judicious mixture of rocks in a finely powdered state. This stone-meal is dry while manure is moist and for that reason the former is worth at least four times as much because more condensed, while in addition thereto the earthy constituents have mostly been eliminated out of the latter by passing through the animal or human body, and the stone-meal mixture contains these in abundance. But of course not all earthy constituents have been taken out of the dung, for of some a superabundance may have been provided, part of which is still contained therein.

Such manure, therefore, is by no means without value; as animal bodies contain about 4-5 of water so there are also considerable quantities of water maintained in crops. Dry hay, e.g., will in the kiln still lose 15% of water; and green fodder and vegetables contain a full 3/4 or 4-5 of water; in some root crops the water amounts even to nine-tenths. Considering its proprieties of water stable manure is not to be valued so highly, because only an equal weight of crops can be procured therefrom. Still even this is sufficient to keep us from rejecting it. Only it should be deprived of the injurious qualities clinging to it owing to its excessive quantity of nitrogen. As far as the liquid manure is concerned, indeed, little damage is done, for despite those erudite in manures the simple farmer spreads the liquid manure over the fields, where the ammonia N_2H_6 is oxidized into nitrogen N_2 and water H_6O_3. Before this process is completed, or at least before the ammonia has been very much diluted, as on the irrigated fields, nothing will grow from it. The most important point lies in this, that it is not the nitrogen which is combined organically with hydrocarbons as in leucin, tyrosin and hippurate of lime which is the most injurious factor of the dunk, but the *carbonate of ammonia*, which is formed from the *urea* of the liquid manure. Free ammonia is a poison to plants.

Ammonia is not only poisonous for plant-roots, but is also poisonous for animals, producing paralysis, even when diluted in the blood to a mere trace. In this respect I shall report a case from actual life respecting stable manure; wherever a similar state prevails a lesson may be drawn from what I report.

In certain cavalry barracks there was a rule that in summer the bedding from the horse stables should be spread in the morning on the open place before the stables to dry, and then be used again in the evening. In the stables of these barracks a remarkable mortality of horses developed, and what was the cause? The liquid manure in the straw became more and more concentrated, and carbonate of ammonia in excessive quantity was thence generated, because urea in a moist state is transformed into this substance.

$$\text{(Urea CO} \begin{matrix} \text{HHH} \\ \text{HHH} \end{matrix} \text{ plus } \text{O} \begin{matrix} \text{H} \\ \text{H} \end{matrix} = \text{COO} \left| \begin{matrix} \text{HHHN} \\ \text{HHHN} \end{matrix} \right. \text{ i.e., carbonate of Ammonia)}$$

Such ammoniacal vapors are indeed perceptible in every horse stable, but in those military stables this evil was extreme. In stepping near the cribs, the rising ammonia vapors irritating the mouth and nostrils caused catarrh, and the eyes would gather tears. Now the heads of the horses were bent down over the cribs, they continually inhaled concentrated fumes of ammonia. This acted in a paralyzing manner on the nervous system. The horses were seized with fever, stopped eating and died. The veterinary physician did not recognize the carbonate of ammonia as the real cause of the appalling numbers of cases of disease and death, but according to his dictum the stables were infected with *Bacilli*. A thorough disinfection with carbolic acid was therefore ordered. For this purpose, of course, the bedding also with all its "bacilli" was ordered out and the learned veterinary physician gained a brilliant scientific victory, for after throwing out and burning the bedding and whitewashing the walls the mortality ceased for the time being.

In my book, *Das Leben,* I have recommended the transformation of the carbonate of ammonia which comes from the liquid manure into odorless sulfate of ammonia and carbonate of lime by strewing the stables with gypsum. Thereby the solid and the liquid manures are freed from their injurious qualities, which are manifested wherever the manure is heaped up a foot deep before it is removed and fresh bedding substituted for it. Those who have hitherto given no heed to the warning fumes of carbonate of ammonia and its evil consequences may continue to consult the veterinarians how to put a stop to the prevalence of cattle diseases.

We have already shown how the carbonate of ammonia may be rendered harmless. Now, in order to largely increase the value of the manure, the primitive rocks containing potassa and soda, reduced to powder, should be scattered over the fields before the manure is spread. Thereby the nitrogenous hydrocarbons of the solid and liquid stable manure are prevented from entering into a decomposing fermentation, which give rise to unwholesome ammoniacal products of decomposition, which in part through capillarity rise into the plants without being transformed into vegetable substance; such plants when cooked manifest an ill odor, as may be seen in vegetables raised on fields irrigated with sewerage. Of late even *roses* are said to be cultivated on such irrigated fields near Berlin, but the home of the Bulgarian rose, that yields the attar of roses, lies at the foot of the Balkan mountains, which consist of granite, gneiss and porphyry; i.e., the rose demands a soil of disintegrated primitive rocks, or with us it demands as a fertilizer pulverized rocks. All roses fertilized with sewerage are infested with leaf-lice. Whoever undertakes rose culture on such fields need not expect success.

In order to lay down once more the value of stable manure, and of crementitious matter in general, it is demonstrable that nitrogenous ammonia is *injurious*. What is effective consists of the combustible *hydrocarbons*, which are ready *building material*, and further of the earthy or *ashy constituents* to which the *hydrocarbons* cling; for the hydrocarbons by themselves are rather injurious than useful to the growth of plants. This may be seen when we pour petroleum on the soil of potted plants, but *hydrocarbon combined with bases and soluble in water* advance the formation of leaves. I summarize them as follows:

1. Nitrogen in the form of carbonate of ammonia is directly injurious to the growth of plants.

2. Nitrogen is *unnecessary* as a fertilizer for the growth of plants if the soil contains a sufficiency of fixed basic substances (alkalies and alkaline earths). The proof of this is afforded by the fruitful calcareous soil of the Jura, which is not manured with nitrogen, so also the illimitable pasture grounds in America as also the vegetation of our German mountains. If plants find at their disposal for their growth a sufficiency of fixed bases they receive an ample supply of the complementary nitrogen from the air, four-fifths of which consists of nitrogen.

3. The nitrogen of the solid and the liquid manure may be used in the construction of plants, but in order to produce crops useful to health it is necessary to add to it a sufficient quality of alkalies and of alkaline earths in the form of stone-meal as a counterpoise. By so doing we not only preserve, but especially amend, the nature of stable manure.

4

WILL FERTILIZING
WITH STONE-MEAL PAY?

Some people say: "With such nonsense as Hensel's 'stone-meal' I shall never have anything to do; nothing *can* grow from it." "Useless dirt." This is the cry of men who have no chemical knowledge, yet two hundred farmers in the Palatinate testified before court that fertilizing with stone-meal showed far better effects than those from the artificial manures used hitherto.

"What do you say to this?" asked the judge of the young man who had declared the stone-meal a swindle (being himself a dealer in artificial manures). "I don't say anything to it, the people deceive themselves," replied the young man, who was fined for a too libelous tongue.

Since then persons who traffic in artificial manures are good enough to allow: "We will not deny that Hensel's stone-meal may have a certain effect, but this is far too slow and too small; for the silicate bases are almost quite insoluble and it will have to disintegrate for many years." These people also are deficient in chemical knowledge.

The silicates have indeed little solubility in water and hydrochloric acid, but they do not resist water and the forces of the sun.

Of course, in speaking of the solubility of silicic acid we must not compare this with the solubility of common salt or sugar. Lime would sooner do for comparison, for of this one part dissolves in 800 parts of water. Silicic acid is somewhat less soluble, for little more than one-half of a grain is dissolved in 1,000 grains of water. All hot springs contain silicic acid in solution together with other substances from the primitive rocks.

Men who say that silicates of bases are insoluble are contradicted by the trees of the forest as well as by every single straw. Oak leaves, on combustion, leave 4 2-3% of ashes, and of these fully one-third consists of silicic acid. How can this come into the leaves unless the ascending sap conveyed it in solution?

The accumulation of the silicic acid in the leaves is the result of the evaporation of the water which conveyed it.

From the forest tree to the straw! In the ashes of the straw of winter wheat, two-thirds consist of silicic acid. In the beard of the barley the proportion is still greater. This yields nearly 12% of ashes, and 8 1/2 of this consists of silicic acid.

Still more striking is the solubility of silicic acid in the stems and leaves of plants which grow in water or in wet soil. Reeds, e.g., on combustion leave 3 1-3% of ashes, more than two-thirds of which is silicic acid.

Sedge or reed-grass yields 6% of ashes, of which one-third is silicic acid. That sedge is at the same time rich in potassa proves in the most striking manner that it needs only irrigation to make silicate of potassa available for plant growth. Shave-grass (Horsetail) leaves 20% of ashes, half of which consist of silicic acid. From this it may be seen that only in those parts of plants which rise above the water, so that evaporation can take place, silicic acid is accumulated. But in the water itself this very solubility of silicic acid stands in the way of its accumulation. The best proof of this we find in seaweed. This leaves behind it a greater proportion of ashes than most plants, namely, up to 14 2-3%, but only one-fiftieth of this is silicic acid. The remainder mainly consists of sulfate and muriate of potassa, soda, lime and magnesia; these the seaweed concentrates and combines with its cellular tissue, for sea water has not 14 2-3% but only about 4% of saline constituents.

This is sufficient to prove that with respect to vegetation silicic acid and silicates are not insoluble; on the contrary, they enter, like all other saline combinations, into the most intimate combination with glycolic acid, C O O C H H, which is intramolecularly present in the cellulose of plants, so also with the ammonia of the chlorophyl so that the silicates cohere with the plants growing from them as an organic whole. We may easily convince ourselves of this on tearing a weed out by its roots. Then it is seen that the root-fibres of most of the plants are everywhere entwined around little stones which, dangling, still cleave to them and can only be torn away from them by violence and by tearing off some of the fibres.

So the objection as to the insolubility of silicic acid is invalid both theoretically and practically.

In reality we cannot find a root, a stem, a leaf or a fruit which does not contain silicic acid. This fact must be known to every teacher of agriculture. How then can these teachers deny the solubility of silicic acid in vegetation, as many of them who advocate artificial fertilizers do?

The men interested in artificial manures who thought that they had attended the funeral of stone-meal as a fertilizer have learned nothing from history, or have at least forgotten that *every* new truth has first to be killed and *buried* before it can celebrate its resurrection. Besides I do not stand as isolated as these people suppose, for I have the light of truth and of knowledge on my side—

> *E'en alone, has strength and might.*
> *He who fights for truth and right.*

I can also call to my aid a whole army of men who understand something of chemistry and of scientific farming, and their number, at this day where science is making such giant strides and hundreds of well edited agricultural papers are ready to support the interests of the farmer, is daily on the increase.

What is lacking at present is that the manufacture of stone-meal should be undertaken by men of scientific attainments who at the same time have sterling honesty, so as to make it certain that farmers will actually receive what is promised and what has proved itself so useful hitherto. I have received innumerable requests from farmers who asked for this mineral manure, but I had to answer them that with my advanced years I could not actively engage in this manufacture. The whole subject is of such immense importance for the common welfare that it is my wish to see this work placed into hands that are *thoroughly reliable*. I but point the way for the benefit of the human race.

The practical point to settle is how far fertilizing with stone meal pays, what yield it will afford, thus whether it will be profitable for the farmer to use it. I shall therefore treat this subject as exhaustively as possible and give an exact account of the results obtained.

It must here be premised that the *fineness of the stamping or grinding and the most complete intermixture* of the constituent parts are of the greatest importance for securing the greatest benefit of stone-meal fertilizing. A manufactured article of this kind has recently been submitted to me which showed in a sieve of moderate fineness three-fourths of the weight in coarse residuum. But as the solubility of the stone-meal, and thus its efficiency, increases in proportion with its fineness, the greatest possible circumspection is required in grinding it. The finer the stone dust the more energetically can the dissolving moisture of the soil and the oxygen and nitrogen of the air act upon it. A grain of stone dust of moderate fineness may be reduced in a mortar of agate perhaps into twenty little particles, and then every little particle may be rendered accessible to the water and the air, and can, therefore, be used as plant food. Thence it follows that one single load of the very finest stone-meal will do as much as twenty loads of a coarser product, so that by reducing to the finest dust the cost for freight and carriage and the use of horse and cart would amount to only one-twentieth. Therefore we can afford to pay unhesitatingly a higher price for the finest stone-meal that has been passed through a sieve than for an article that may be not so much a fine powder but rather a kind of coarse sand.

The average contents of ash in cereals is about 3%. Thence, from three pounds of pure vegetable ashes we could raise a hundred pounds of crops. Now, as stone-meal properly made contains an abundance of plant food in assimilable form, it may be calculated to produce four cwt. of cereals, or that an annual use of six cwt. to the acre will produce twenty-four cwt. of grain. On this basis every farmer can calculate whether it will pay. But in reality the harvest will be far greater, because even without the stone-meal most fields still possess some supply of mineral nutriment for plants which will become effective in addition thereto. Such being the case we need not consider the fact that not all the stone-meal is used up completely in the first year, but yields nourishment to plants even in the fifth year, as has been shown by experiments. That no mistake would be made by using double the quantity on an acre, or twelve cwt. instead of six, is manifest, for the prospects of a still greater yield would thereby be improved, but in applying twelve cwt. an abundance would be supplied; even five or six times that quantity would be far from causing an injury to the soil, but we cannot force by excessive quantities of stone-meal a correspondingly higher yield of crops for the reason that within a definite area only a definite quantity of sunlight can display its activity, and on this factor the growth of the crop mainly depends. There is, therefore, no use in passing beyond a certain quantity of mineral manure; it could only come into use in subsequent years, and it appears to be more practical to supply the amount needed each year.

I will now present in summary form the quintessence of the significance of this natural fertilizer.

1. The point to be gained is not only a *greater quantity* of produce, but also a *better quality*. Sugar-beets gain thereby more sugar, this, according to experiments made, may amount to 75% more than hitherto. Potatoes and cereals show a greater proportion of *starch*. Oil crops (as poppies, rape, etc.) show more seed-vessels and a corresponding increase in *oil*. Pulse, such as beans, peas, etc., yields more *lechithin* (oil containing phosphate of am-

monia as the chemical basis of nerve-substance). Fruits and all vegetables receive a more delicate *flavor*. (The vegetables in my garden have become famous with our neighbors and our guests, so that they ask: "How do you manage that?") Meadows furnish grass and hay of more *nutritive value*. Vines form *stronger shoots,* give *sweeter grapes* and are *not touched* by *insects* and *fungus diseases*.

2. The soil is steadily built up and improved by this natural fertilizer, as it is progressively *normalized,* i.e., shows gathered together potassa, soda, lime, magnesia, fluorine, and phosphoric and sulfuric acid, etc., in the most favorable combination. There is hardly *one* cultivated field which by nature is normal at the present. Either lime prevails or we have a clayey soil, which through its excess of clay refuses to let the rain water pass, and by its toughness obstructs the access of the atmospheric nitrogen and of the carbonic acid; or we have a mere sandy soil (quartz), or again the soil has humus in excess, like moor-land soil. This latter is characterized by a predominance of lime and magnesia on the one side, while sulfuric bases are two or three times in excess of phosphatic bases, as is shown by the analysis of the ashes of peat.

3. The value of the new fertilizer with respect to the wholesomeness of nutritive plants and fodder depends in great part on the careful and intimate comixture of its several constituents, so that with very little dust of potassa and soda the other nutritive elements required to co-operate in the harmonic construction of plants are at their disposal in proximate vicinity. As a contrast to this, in a one-sided fertilizing with lime it may happen that the plant contents itself with the lime so that the other constituents of the soil are not drawn into co-operation for the growth of the produce, because they are not within the nearest proximity of the root-fibres. This is, of course, of great importance to the quality and the nutritive value of the plants.

4. For raising nutritive plants and fodder which may afford *wholesome nourishment* I deem it of the greatest importance that no substances should be used which lead to *ammoniacal decomposition*. By such additions we may indeed produce a luxuriant, excessive growth that blinds the eyes and in which the abundant

formation of leaves by means of nitrogen forms the chief part; but no healthy growth is effected thereby. From this point of view I would also deprecate the use of so-called fish guano. Everyone knows how quickly fish pass over into putrefaction: there is formed at the same time a considerable quantity of *propylamin* (C_3H_6,NH_3) which is an *ammoniacal base*. The manure manufactured in Sweden from fish-guano and powdered feldspar does not, therefore, merit the esteem that it claims.

5

A CHAPTER FOR CHEMISTS

The Chemical Process in the Growth of Plants Which are the Basis of our Nutrition.

"Every leaf in the hedge sings to the wise
An excerpt from the wondrous lay of Creation!"

The sum and substance of the growth of plants consists in creating out of burnt substances through the electrically-decomposing forces of the sun material which may again be burned.

Take an example: A stearine candle, consisting of hydrocarbons (C H H), in a twenty-four fold aggregation, is consumed by means of the oxygen of the air into carbonic acid or carbon dioxide (C O O) and water (H H O) and these same products of combustion may through the vegetation processes in plants be again wholly or partially changed back into hydrocarbons. This is effected by separating from the carbonic acid dissolved in rain water or combined with the moisture in the soil, water and together with this oxidized water (peroxide of hydrogen). In this way there arise from two molecules of carbonic acid and two of water, first of all oxalic acid ($C_2H_2O_4$) and peroxide of hydrogen (O H H O).

$$\left.\begin{array}{l} C\,O\,O, H\,H\,O \\ C\,O\,O, H\,H\,O \end{array}\right| = \left.\begin{array}{l} C\,O\,O\,H \\ C\,O\,O\,H \end{array}\right| \begin{array}{l} H\,O. \\ H\,O. \end{array}$$

The peroxide of hydrogen passes into the atmosphere decomposed into watery vapor and oxygen, while oxalic acid arising as the first product of the reduction of carbonic acid caused by the action of the sun is found combined with lime in all vegetable cells. Formerly this first *process of growth* (for oxalic acid arises from the *accretion* of two atoms of hydrogen to two molecules of carbonic acid) was not at all understood. It is hardly four years ago that I heard a teacher of agricultural economy say: "Lime has no value in the growth of plants, it is rather injurious than beneficial. The plant knows not at all what to do with the lime; in order to rid itself more easily of it, it takes up as oxalate of lime in the cells."

Oxalic acid derives its name from the fact that chemists first discovered it in woodsorrel (Oxalis) in the form of a combination of oxalic acid with lime. From the oxalic acid there proceeds in a continuous reduction *sugar, the material of plant-cells and starch.*

The sugar that has been produced from a symmetrical grouping of two molecules of hydrocarbons, two of carbonic acid and two of water.

$$\begin{array}{c|c} \begin{array}{l} H\,O\,H \\ H\,C\,H \\ H\,C\,H \\ O\,C\,O \end{array} & \begin{array}{l} H\,O\,H \\ H\,C\,H \\ H\,C\,H \\ O\,C\,O \end{array} \end{array}$$

and which, therefore, is not yet a complete product of reduction, produces with the separation of carbonic acid and of water through a heaped up grouping together of hydrocarbons, which remain yet combined with a molecule of formic acid, COO HH (this second product of production or rather product of addition to carbonic acid), then the vegetable *oils* (olive oil, almond oil, poppy oil, rapeseed oil, linseed oil, etc.)

Furthermore from sugar, which is exhibited in all young plants during their sprouting after receiving water vapor and nitrogen from the air, and, indeed, after again separating peroxide of hydrogen, while ammonia arises there are formed $N_2H_{12}O_6NH_6H_6O_6$ the numerous kinds of *vegetable albumen*.

The simplest kind of vegetable albumen is found in asparagus, in the juice of asparagus.

O		HH		O		HH
C		CC		C		NNHH
O		HH		O		HH

a combination of ammonia with malic acid, which is a step towards the formation of sugar or rather a product of splitting off from sugar.

This asparagin is found not only in asparagus, but to select an example which may easily be demonstrated also in the young roots of thistles (which are weeded out from asparagus beds) and which taste very much like raw asparagus, and it is also found in the sprouts of very many other plants.

As the simplest of all kinds of vegetable albumen asparagus is the best exemplification of the fact that in albumen intramolecular *gelatine sugar* is contained:

$$
\begin{array}{ccc}
H & O & H \\
C & C & NH \\
H & O & H
\end{array}
$$

Of the latter, however, it is acertained that on account of its contents of carbonic acid it can condense into an organic whole with itself *basic* substance (potassa, soda, magnesia, oxide of iron and oxide of manganese), and owing to its basic ammoniacal substratum it also condenses *acids*, and accordingly also at the same time both bases and acids (e.g., sulfate of magnesia, phosphate of lime, the silicates of potash and of soda, fluorate of lime), besides manganese and oxide of iron, and there arise indeed on account of the contents of the hydrocarbon (H C H) in the gelatine sugar from insoluble substances soluble combinations after the analogy of the insoluble sulfate of baryta and the ethyl sulfate of baryta which is soluble in water.

And so we may comprehend how from earthy elements in combination with sugar and nitrogen there can arise in endless modifications the most numerous varieties of vegetable albumen, according as the soil furnishes various substances.

In this the electrolyte force of the sun plays the part of the architect. Like as in the galvanic bath the atoms of the reduced metals apply themselves into a connected covering without a gap, so the solar forces cement together the reduced elements of the hydrocarbons with phosphates, sulfates, muriates, fluorates, silicates and carbonates of lime, of potash, soda, magnesia, and of the oxides of manganese and iron together into the edifices which, as grasses, herbs, bushes, and trees, refresh our eyes with their leaves and flowers, while their fruits serve to nourish man as well as the animal world.

But it is to be noticed that the above-mentioned processes only take place under the supposition that the carbonic acid, which lays the foundation out of which the hydrocarbons arise, find basic substances (potash, soda, lime, magnesia, etc.) with which they can condense themselves into firm combinations. Therefore the firm earth is the absolute condition for all vegetable growth, there is no vegetation in the air alone; nor must water be lacking (H H O), for its hydrogen (H H) being combustible in itself renders the groups of hydrocarbons combustible.

Now, as the process of our life represents nothing else than a continual combustion of our bodily substance by means of the oxygen respired, with the condition that to replace the substance consumed during the day by oxidation, during the night new combustible material must be supplied; by the contents rich in soil of the lymphatic vessels to the numerous sheaths as the oil of life, and to the renewing blood new albuminous substance. Our life could not continue if we should not renew so much of the bodily material as is chemically consumed by the oxidizing respiration by means of the periodic supply of food. Every disturbance in the regular supply of food has the most manifest effects on the state of the soil. The inexorable demand for new material in place of the bodily substance which is breathed away makes even men, who by nature are kindly, angry and regardless of others when their food is kept back. And so cause and effect join themselves into a mischievous chain.

As the means for procuring food consists in by far the greater number of callings in coined money, and this is only given as a reward for work done, the question arises: What can the man do who has no opportunity and chance to find paying work? He will and must eat. If we can assist every one in getting a supply of food the mainspring for lying, deceit, stealing and numerous crimes vanishes.

Food is supplied to us in the first place by the immediate produce of the ground, and only in the second place by the fat, flesh and blood of domestic animals produced from grasses and herbs.

Now, as it is a primary chemical condition that earthy material, air, water and solar forces must be present in order that plants may grow, it is the all-mother Earth which, surrounded by water and earth and fructified by sunshine, nourishes men and animals through the crops produced: and at the same time it clothes animals, as their skin causes the hair to sprout forth, which contains sulfur and silicea, and the hair by isolating keeps together the bodily warmth and the bodily electricity.

Man, whose producing spirit desires occupation and to whom is granted the wonderful mechanism of the fingers, has the advantage that he can weave his garments according to the season, either of flax and cotton or of the wool of sheep and the hair of goats, and can protect himself from the wind, the weather and the cold by using the wood from the forest to build his house and to warm it.

Food, clothing and shelter are the fundamental requirements to which everyone born has a claim, and these can also be acquired by every one who has sound limbs. In the muscles of our arms we possess the fairy charm which can say: "Table be set!" for labor always finds its reward. Of course if people are foolish enough to leave the places where the muscles of their arms are in demand and paid for, if they leave the source of all earthly riches, agriculture, and go where their arms have no value, because many others that are unemployed are waiting for employment, then distress, lack of food, of clothing and shelter must give him the occasion to consider and turn back, returning to a life in the country, which is continually becoming more deprived of its inhabitants.

Every work brings its reward. Work is necessary for our bodily and mental well-being. By co-operation it confirms us in the consciousness of a common humanity, for in social life we see in every fellowman an image of ourselves and this calls for mutual regard, charity, kindliness, mutual assistance. How different with the man who is not working. His thoughts turn to laying nets and setting traps in which to catch his unsuspecting fellowmen.

Further, when the knowledge will have spread more and more that the essential work of man consists in allowing the sun to work for him, in order that food, raiment and wood may grow up from earth, water and air, then many foolish outbirths of idle brains will lose their soil and foundation.

There are, indeed, in these times some bad calculators who say: We will work less and get more money. These do not consider that the more money is in circulation, so much more money must be paid for the materials of food, if these remain the same in quantity, and this change will be of indefinite limits. The real remedy can only consist *in producing more food.* The more grain is raised, the less money will be required to pay it. Here we must apply our lever. What infatuation, when men attack one another in order to compel the supply of sufficient food. That can only be furnished by the earth. "Does a cornfield grow in my palm?" God has created us rich enough in supplying us with an understanding. If we use this, brother need not overreach brother, but we can in serene tranquility of soil win the little that we need day by day from our all-mother Earth.

6

STONE-MEAL AS
A TOBACCO FERTILIZER

Of late years the general attention of tobacco growers centered in the query, "What is the best manure for obtaining a good tobacco?" For it stands to reason that, if for a number of years tobacco is grown on the same fields, in the course of time the soil must be rendered bare of the constituents entering into the remarkable quantity of ash which tobacco contains. There is no other product of the soil which gives as much ashes as does tobacco, for the best dried leaves will yield from 14 to 27%, while, for example, dried ash or beech leaves only yield 4 3/4%, and most other plants contain still less, dried pine needles only 1 1/4%. In the ash of most plants yielding 2% or more silex predominates ash and beech ashes containing over one-third, while the ash of barley and oat straw consists of one-half of silex. It is, however, quite different with tobacco ash, which contains only one-twentieth part of silex, the rest being lime, magnesia, potash, soda, phosphoric and sulfuric acid. There is no fixed rule in the proportion of these substances, but lime and potash always predominate in about the proportion of five to four parts.

German tobacco yields less ash than Virginia leaf, only about 14%, and consists of about five parts of lime, four of potash, one of magnesia, one-half of soda, two-thirds of phosphoric acid, four-fifths of sulfuric acid, four-fifths of silex and one part of muriatic acid.

The less of sulfuric and muriatic acid a tobacco contains the freer will it burn and the whiter its ash will be. The best tobacco is raised with nothing but wood ashes for manure, and be it noted that the ashes of oak, beech, birch, pine and fir contain not a trace of muriatic acid and but 1/50% of sulfuric acid. We are forced, therefore, to the inevitable conclusion that the comparatively high percentage of sulfuric and muriatic acid which the ash of German tobacco yields and which makes its present quality so poor is owing to the persistent use of *stable manure*, and it is plainly of the utmost importance to do without that altogether.

The question now arises what shall be used in its stead? Our answer is, that inasmuch as forest trees are grown on rocky soil which contain *potash, soda, lime* and *magnesia* in combination with *silica alumina* and *phosphoric acid* we must, instead of burning the expensive trees for the purpose of obtaining their ashes for tobacco manure, go back to the original substances out of which the trees were created, and these are suitable minerals found in the rocks. This is as plain a proposition as the egg of Columbus.

With regard to Virginia tobacco a study of the topographical features of the tobacco lands will be in order. The best soil for the purpose is found where the debris of the Alleghenies and their foot hills the blue mountains has been washed down into the plain. These mountains contain gneiss, granite, syenite, serpentine and hornblende slate. Hornblende is silicea combined with lime magnesia an iron. In syenite lime and magnesia predominate over potash and soda; Virginia gneiss abounds in lime, magnesia and iron. These lime and magnesia silicates are of far more importance for the production of a fine tobacco which will burn freely making a white and firm ash than the potash which is found in all primitive rocks, although potash is necessary for the production of elastic leaf cells so much appreciated in good tobacco. But it is a great mistake to lay undue stress on an over-abundance of potash. Neither the Strassfurt potash salts nor powdered iron slag will produce good tobacco. For the potash contained in tobacco is not combined therein with sulfuric and muriatic acid, but enters into direct combination with cell material, and it is eliminated out of silicated potash and soda by the action of the carbonic acid of the air or of the soil. A healthy and fine quality of tobacco can therefore only be grown by the use of a liberal supply of a mineral mixture which yields in appropriate proportions silicate of potash and soda together with carbonate of lime and magnesia and a small proportion of phosphoric acid, such as was present originally in the virgin soil of the tobacco lands of Virginia.

In accordance with these principles suitable mixtures of the several kinds of rocks have been prepared in the form of very fine powder for the production of fine tobacco, and it is at present being used with great success in the Palatinate of Germany.

7

A PAPER CONTRIBUTED TO THE *DEUTSCHES ADELSBLATT*, JANUARY 31st, 1892

In cereals, in the seeds of the leguminous plants, and of the oil-bearing plants, the mineral substances with which the cellular tissue and the vegetable albumen are combined constitute from 17 to 50 thousand. After the combustion of plant tissue these mineral constituents remain behind as ashes, and the greater part of the ashes in the seeds consist of *phosphoric acid* and *potassa*, while soda, lime, magnesia, hydrochloric acid, sulfuric and silicic acid with manganese; iron and fluorine are comparatively less in quantity. Only in the oil-producing seeds (mustard, rapeseed, linseed, hempseed and poppyseed) lime and magnesia make a considerable part of the ashes. The following numerical proportion will give a general view:

Winter Wheat has on the average 16 8-10 thousandths of ashes, of which phosphoric acid forms 7 9-10 thousandths and 5 2-10 of potassa.

Field Beans yield 31 thousandths of ashes, of which phosphoric acid forms 16 2-10, potassa 7, lime 18 and magnesia 5 thousandths.

Poppyseed gives 51 5-10 thousandths of ashes, of which 16 2-10 are phosphoric acid, potassa 7, lime 18 and magnesia 5.

From the fact that phosphoric acid and potassa have such a prominence in nutritive crops, it was easy to draw this conclusion: *"That potassa and phosphoric acid are the most necessary fertilizers and the more phosphoric acid the better."* But this conclusion is erroneous and has caused us much injury since Liebig made this statement.

Liebig and his successors have overlooked the fact, that in the time of vegetation phosphoric acid is so uniformly distributed that it does not amount in the average to more than one-tenth of the mineral constituents. If during the process of ripening phosphoric acid strongly accumulates in the seeds, that it constitutes not merely 10, but 30 to 50% of the ashes, this is explained by the fact that the acid passes from the stems, stalks and leaves into the seeds, leaving the straw very poor in phosphoric acid, as may appear from these proportions:

(a.) *The straw of winter wheat* has in the average 46 thousandths of ashes, of which only 2 2-10, thus about 1-20 or 5% consist of phosphoric acid. The rest consists of 6 potassa, 0.6 soda, 2.7 lime, 1.1 magnesia, 1.1 sulfuric acid, 0.8 hydrochloric acid and 31 thousandths of silicic acid. The latter (silica) only amounts to 0.3 of one thousandth in the wheat grain thus in comparison with the straw only one-thousandth.

(b.) *The straw of field bean* furnishes 45 thousandths of ashes, of which there are only phosphoric acid, thus 1-15 or 6 1/2%, while in the ashes of the seeds it constitutes 36%. The other substances contained in bean straw are 19.4 thousandths potassa, 0.8 soda, 12 lime, 2.6 magnesia, 1.8 sulfuric acid, 2.0 hydrochloric acid and 3.2 silicic acid. On account of this small quantity of silica bean straw is *soft*, while wheat straw, rich in silica, is hard.

(c.) The straw of *poppy* gives about 48 1/2 thousandths of ashes, of which there are only 1.6 of phosphoric acid; i.e., in *poppy straw* phosphoric acid constitutes only 1-30 of the ashes, while in the seeds it amounts to 1/3. So considerable, amounting to the ten-fold, is the difference. The rest of the ashes of the straw of poppy consists of 18.4 potassa, 0.6 soda, 14.7 lime, 3.1 magnesia, 2.5 sulfuric acid, 1.3 hydrochloric acid and 5.5 silicic acid.

The examples adduced are to a certain degree typical of cereals, leguminous plants and oil-yielding plants and they explain why leguminous and oily plants need more lime in the soil than cereals. On the whole, when we take the average of 70 or 80 analyses of field-crops, which also include the roots, stems and leaves, we come to the conclusion that phosphoric acid constitutes about one-tenth of the mineral constituents, while potassa, soda, lime, magnesia, silica, sulfuric acid, chlorine and fluorine contribute the remaining nine-tenths. Furthermore, potassa and soda are present on the average in the same amount of weight as lime and magnesia. These four bases amount to about eight-tenths of the whole quantity of the ashes, and it is found in practice that these bases may to a considerable degree act as substitutes for one another, without perceptibly varying the form and the organic constituents of these plants.

According to these facts a fertilizer which would satisfy the natural demand of supplying the minerals necessary for the construction of plants should contain to one part of phosphoric acid eight parts of potassa, soda, lime and magnesia, if we are willing to leave out of our count phosphoric, hydrochloric and silicic acid.

Such a fertilizer, however, is found in every primitive rock. Primitive rocks do not, indeed, contain more than 1% of phosphoric acid, but that is quite sufficient; it is, indeed, the measure wisely appointed by the Creator of all things, for the other constituents of granite, porphyry, etc., which serve for the nourishment of plants, consist of about 6% of potassa and soda and 2% of lime and magnesia. The residue of the rock serves as a substance dispersed between the basic substances to keep them apart, and they are dissolved out of their combination with silicic acid only as they are applied to use. Thence we receive such wholesome cereals from mountainous countries; e.g., from Hungary, encircled by the Carpathian Mountains, in contrast with the prevalence of diseases due to the decomposition of the blood of men and of animals in the exhausted plains which are supplied with stable manure.

If we wish to grasp quickly and completely the correctness and importance of mineral manure, we need only to consider the cases of Uruguay and Argentina or of Egypt; or, to mention an example from our proximate vicinity, that of the principality of Birkenfeld.

In Uruguay and Argentina the livestock is estimated at about thirty-two millions (beeves, sheep and horses). Of these there are now killed for export every year about one and a quarter million and the bones of these animals are carried by the shiploads to Hamburg, in order to be worked up into bone-black to be used in the sugar refineries. It is self-evident that the animals take the phosphate of lime for their bones and the nitrogen for their flesh and for the glue in their bones from the grass they eat. But the grass draws the necessary nitrogen from the air, for they use no fertilizers, and the phosphate of lime, which continually passes from the country in the form of bones, is received by the grass from the inexhaustible calvareous porphyritic mud which is carried down through millions of gorges from the Cordilleras by the mountain streams and which flows as a primitive manure into the eastern plains. In Egypt this is effected by the Nile mud, which the mountain streams bring down, and which is conveyed by the Nile in fructifying abundance to the Delta, which thereby becomes the becomes the granary of Egypt.

But we need not go so far even. The little principality of Birkenfeld demonstrates the fertility of the primary rocks which the mountains of the Hundsruechen supplies in the form of argillaceous slate. It is a little Argentina. The trade in cattle plays an important part in Birkenfeld. Besides these oil factories, linen factories and beer breweries prove that cereals and oil plants, rich in phosphorus, and among them flax, rich in potassa, find there good nutritive supplies. The forests consist mainly of deciduous trees and harbor much game. Trees need phosphoric acid for their roots, trunks and bark, and the game needs phosphate of lime for the bones. The ashes of oak wood and beech wood contain 6% of phosphoric acid, and that of the horse-chestnut contains 7%. So richly does the argillaceous slate furnish the nutrious elements for the growth of plants and especially the right quantity of phosphoric acid.

In contrast with these natural fertilizers what has our prudent and learned fertilizing with phosphoric acid effected? It has brought it about that we don't know how to save ourselves from the phylloxera, the nematodes, hay-worm, spring-worm and sour-worm nor from the fungi causing rust and great quantities of it. A gladsome, luxuriant growth and a rich yield of grapes are *not* produced, though we furnish the grapevines with the potassa, phosphoric acid and nitrogen in so great quantities that the shoots, the grapes and the leaves ought to display the utmost luxuriance; but instead of this everything in the vineyards here looks sickly and poor. I should, therefore, be very glad and grateful to you if you would give us your views about this. It would be a great benefit, not only to ourselves, but to the whole of the Rheingan, and wherever grape-vines are cultivated, to be delivered from the miseries of the spring-worm, hay-worm and sour-worm, the phylloxera and the *Peronospora viticola*, and if this can be done by your method all cultivators of the grapevine will exclaim: "God be praised!"

I answered that the usual manure does not lack any necessary ingredients, but there is in it *too much of some things*, i.e., of nitrogen and phosphoric acid. Men must return to the original material, restore to the soil its natural original qualities by bringing to the fields soil that has not been exhausted, which may be done in the form of powdered primitive rocks mingled with sulfates and carbonates of lime and magnesia. The correctness of such belief is attested by the following correspondence with a landscape gardener and nursery man from the Rheinprovinz:

"We would like to ask you for some information as to what we had best use for manuring our nurseries. We have clayey, deep, light soil, formerly a forest. We cultivate roses, fruit trees and forest trees, also evergreen plants, firs and various kinds of cypresses. It is quite peculiar that quinces and other fruits (Formobst) in the second year after grafting absolutely refuse to grow any more despite of the use of stable manure, iron slag or of Chili nitre."

I answered that deep clayey forest soil while retaining its clay and silica has been deprived of its basic constituents (potassa, soda, lime and magnesia) which in the process of time have passed over into the wood of the roots and of the trunks, and that the only thing promising relief is fresh rock meal. For are not the Balkan countries the home of the *roses*, and do not the Haemus Mountains consist of porphyry, granite and gneiss, but not of stable manure and clay? Do not cypresses grow in the regions of the Apennines, which furnish the nourishing material from their granite and gneiss. And do not firs grow on mountains of granite and porphyry? Finally *fruit*? The Bohemian Mountains furnished it in abundance, and indeed free from worms. This latter fact, that the use of stone-meal causes worms to cease, was lately confirmed by Mr. Fischer, M.D., of Westend, near Charlottenburg, who introduced stone-meal manure two years ago in his garden, situated on a sandy soil. He reported about it in the January number of the *Deutsche Pomologen-Verein*.

From a third letter I quote as follows:

"*Manor L.*—I am glad to see a chemist who has the courage to openly oppose the swindle of the artificial manures. Within a series of ten years I bought at least $17,000 worth of artificial fertilizers, of which sum over $6,000 were paid for Chili nitre. I harvested more every year; but what? Nothing but straw, lodged grain and cereals of low grade. For the last two years I have bought, in addition, animal manure and lime, and I find that at a slight expense everything is being changed and that the field will again bring in what I lost in former years. When the Thomas phosphate was introduced, as it was cheap, I used at once 2,000 cwt. With 7 cwt. per acre an effect was indeed seen, but what was it that acted? Surely only the lime. What you have affirmed I have long felt. That many of us agriculturists are faring so badly is for the most part owing to this nuisance of our artificial, expensive and useless fertilizers."

A fourth letter with an excerpt, of which I will conclude, contains the following:

"Twenty years ago, while in office in Alsatia, I endeavored to make myself acquainted and familiar with all manner of subjects.

I was led to the idea of mineral fertilizers or manures, when I heard and saw that in the intersecting valleys of the Vosges Mountains the winter torrents covered the lowlands with granite debris, which after a few years became very fruitful soil; but I had no opportunity or occasion to follow out this idea any further, which is now, however the case." (G. L., Privy Councillor of war a D.)

Every such letter contains new confirmatory facts; I have quite a collection of such correspondence, but will not weary you by quoting more.

Julius Hensel.

Hermsdorf unterm Kynast.

8

STONE-MEAL MANURE

(*Pioneer*, July 22, 1892)

"Bread from stones: and thus forsooth
The Bible words maintain their truth."

I have before this taken occasion, in the *Deutsche Adelsblatt*, to show that calling the stone dust "manure" is really not correct, as it is superior to the so-called manures in this that it restores the natural conditions for the growth of crops, while manures only present an artificial help and thus a makeshift. The whole state of the case is as follows:

In the beginning plants grew without any artificial addition from the soil formed of disintegrated material from the mountains. The carbonic acid of the air combined with the basic constituents, potassa, soda, lime, magnesia, iron and manganese, which were combined in the disintegrated rock-material with silicic acid, alumina, sulfur, phosphorus, chlorine and fluorine, and with the co-operation of moisture by the operation of the heat and light of the sun it produced vegetable cell-tissue. The gaseous substances, *carbonic acid* (carbon dioxide), *watery vapor* and the nitrogen of the air acquire the firm forms of vegetable cellular tissue and vegetable albumen solely through the basic foundation of potassa, soda, lime and magnesia, without which no root, stalk, leaf or fruit is found; for whether we burn the leaves of maples or of beech trees, the roots of burdocks or of willows, grains of rye or wood, straw or linen, pears, cherries or rapeseed, there always remains a residuum of ashes which, in various proportions, consists of potassa, soda, lime, magnesia, iron, manganese, phosphoric acid, sulfuric acid, fluorine and silica. With respect to *nitrogen*, this with watery vapor forms in the presence of iron—which is present in all soils—becomes according to the formula $N_2H_6O_3Fe_2=N_2H_6Fe_2O_3$ (all iron-rust that is formed in the nightly dew out of metallic iron Fe_2O_3, contains ammonia, as Eilard Mitscherlich has proved). The solidification of the cellular tissue arising from carbonic acid and water will be best understood by comparing it with the process of the formation of hard soap by the combination of oil with soda, potassa, lime or any other basic substance, as, e.g., oxide of lead, quicksilver or iron. Ammonia also forms soap with oxidized oil, oleic acid. We can hardly find any better comparison by which to explain the solidification of the atmospheric vapors (carbonic acid, water, nitrogen and oxygen) in combination with earthy substances or in substitution for the latter with ammonia into vegetable substance than on the one side this process, of saponification and on the other hand the oil-substance which is the basis of soap. The production of oil substance consists in this that combustible substances (hydrocarbons) are generated from burned-up substances (carbonic acid and water), and this characterizes in the main the nature of the universal vegetation of plants. A burning stearine candle is transformed into carbonic acid gas and watery vapor, but these aeriform products, in combination with earths, are again transmuted into combustible wood, sugar, starch and oil by the operation of the sun. Wherever new earth comes into activity, as at the foot of mountains, there is found a vigorous growth of plants, especially when a sufficiency of carbonic acid clings to the rock as in the Jura regions. The road from Basel to Biel is very instructive in this respect. On the contrary, it is seen that in densely populated regions as, e.g., in China and Japan, after a cultivation of many thousands of years, the earth, exhausted of the material that forms cells, is of itself unwilling to produce as many nutritive plants as men and animals need for their sustenance; but as had been perceived that the nourishment which has been consumed, in so far as it has not been used in the new formation of lymphatic fluid and blood, being therefore superfluous, leaves the body through the digestive canal although chemically disintegrated and putrefied, nevertheless produces new vegetation when this material is brought on the fields and is mixed with earth; in China they collect with great care not only whatever has passed through the intestinal canal, but also the product of the bodily substance which is consumed by respiration, which is eliminated as the secretion of the kidneys and which also gives an impulse to new growth.

One or the other must take place. Either unexhausted new soil or the restoration of the nutrition consumed to the soil of the fields. Where the latter has not been done, as by the first European settlers in America, the crops decreased and the settlers moved from the east further to the west, in order to gain enough cereals from the as yet unexhausted soil for export to Europe. Now they have also come to see in America that they cannot continue thus, as there are no more domains without owners into which they can emigrate without let or hindrance.

But how is it with us in Germany in this respect? After the soil would not yield any more, despite of deep plowing, the circle instituted in China was also put into practice. They had to see that the solid and liquid manure of the domestic animals brought on the fields produced a new growth, and the dungheaps began to be valued. By the aid of this dung the fields were kept fertile, although this was a mere makeshift. This makeshift has become a familiar one for several centuries, so that even in the times of our great-grandfathers the saying was in vogue: "Where there is no manure nothing will grow." So eventually what was a mere makeshift has become the regular rule. As a consequence of this traditional view the conclusion followed: In order to get a large quantity of manure we must keep as many cattle as practicable. In this it was overlooked that the cattle would require again as much acreage for their nutrition, and the ground thus used could not be used to raise grain, so that in such an economy it was necessary to work the fields for the sake of the cattle, not for the sake of the men. But finally the thoughtful and book-keeping farmers had to come to the conclusion that the raising of cattle only pays in mountainous districts, or in districts like the marshes of Holstein, which are kept fruitful by the continual washing down of Geest rocks.

I can only summarize here. As above said, the dungheap had been recognized as the augmenter of fertility, and dungheaps were considered as the natural condition, *sine quo non*, for the growth of crops, although this was by no means founded on the natural order, but was only a makeshift. When once the rule was established that the artificial was normal we need not be surprised that when the stable manure would no more suffice some people recommended *artificial manure*. As these people gave themselves great airs of learning the well-educated, large land-owners fell into their net, even more than the simple peasants, and therewith the general retrocession of agricultural produce in the level regions was for some time at least fixed and sealed.

It may easily be seen that oxen and cows, no matter how high their cost, charged no salary for producing their manure. It was otherwise with the chemists and the dealers in artificial manure. These not only demanded to be nourished themselves, but also desired from the gain produced by their business to educate their children, to build their magazines, to pay their traveling agents and to increase their capital. This business, like all those which supply necessaries, proved so remunerative that one of the greatest houses dealing in artificial manures in a short time had made millions, which were paid them by the farmers without receiving an equivalent; for in spite of the most energetic application of artificial manures the crops steadily decreased. How could it be otherwise? Plants need potassa, soda, lime, magnesia, iron, manganese, sulfur, phosphorus and fluorine, and in the artificial fertilizers they only received expensive potassa, phosphoric acid and nitrogen for their nourishment.

The consequence of this showed itself first of all in frequent bankruptcies of agriculturists. But besides this, nitrogenous fertilizers in the form of Chili-nitre have caused a predominance of cattle diseases. That hares and deer have been found dead in numbers in places which had been fertilized with Chili-nitre I have read in at least twenty newspapers, and it has also been reported to me by eye-witnesses. As in the open air so also in the stables. No normal animal bodily substance can be formed from fodder manured with nitrogen, especially no wholesome milk equal to that from cows feeding on mountain herbs.

It is not to be computed how great an injury to health with men and animals has been caused by stable manure. Milk produced from ammoniacal plants paved the way by which the destructive spirit diphtheria has swooped down after measles, scarlatina, scrofula, pneumonia had become the familiar companions of the Germans, who before were strong as bears. Artificial manure at last put the crown on this work of destruction.

How could this happen? Very simply. *Liebig* was the first agricultural chemist. He found that the ashes which remained from grain mainly consisted of phosphate of potassa. From this he concluded that phosphate of potassa must be restored to the soil, and that was very one-sided. Liebig had forgotten to take the straw into account, in which only small quantities of phosphoric acid are found, because this substance during the process of maturing passes from the stalk into the grain. If he had not only calculated the seed but also the roots and the stalks, he would have found what we know at this day, that in the whole plants there is as much lime and magnesia as potassa and soda, and that phosphoric acid forms only the tenth part of the sum of these basic constituents. Unfortunately Liebig also was of the opinion that potassa and phosphoric acid has to be restored to the soil as such, while any one might have concluded that instead of the exhausted soil we must supply earthy material from which nothing has been grown. Such untouched earthy material of primitive strength we get by pulverizing rocks in which potassa, soda, lime, magnesia, manganese, and iron are combined with silica, alumina, phosphoric acid, fluorine and sulfur. Among these substances fluorine, which is found in all mica-minerals, has been neglected by Liebig and by all his followers, and has never been contained in any artificial manure. But as we know from later investigations that fluorine is regularly found even in the white and yellow of birds' eggs, we must acknowledge it is something essential to the organism. Chickens get this fluorine and the other earthy constituents when they have a chance to pick up little slivers of granite. Where this is denied them, as in a wooden hen house, they succumb to chicken cholera and chicken diphtheria.

We men are not as well off as the birds of the heavens. We must eat the soup prepared for us by the dealers in artificial manures. Since these sell no fluorine our cereals suffer a lack in fluorine, and as no normal bony substance can be formed without fluorine in the same degree as the number of dealers in fertilizers increased the army of dentists and the erection of orthopedic institutes increased; but the latter were unable to remove the curvature of the spine in our children. The enamel of the teeth needs fluorine, the albumen and the yolk of the eggs require fluorine, the bones of the spine require fluorine, the pupil of the eye also needs fluorine. It is not by accident that Homeopathy cures numerous affections of the eye with fluoride of calcium.

How rich, how strong and how healthy will we Germans be when we make our mountains tributary to yield new soil from which new wholesome cereals may be formed. We need then no more to send our savings to Russia, to Hungary, to America, but will make our way through life by our strong elbows and with German courage, and shall keep off our adversaries.

The goal aimed at, of satisfying the hungry, and of preventing numerous maladies by restoring the natural condition for wholesome plant growth, seems to me one of the highest and the most noble. Even six hundredweight of prepared stone-dust to the Prussian *morgen* (= one fourth hectare, or about 10 hundredweight to the acre) will give sufficient nourishment for a satisfactory crop, if this amount is supplied every year. If more is used, the yield may be so much the more increased.

I concluded these remarks, which were introduced with a motto that adorned the exhibit in Leipzig of the produce yielded by stone-dust, by reproducing also the second rhyme which had been introduced there, and which, like the motto, has a conscientious adherent of mineral manure for its author:

> "Art we love, but never can endure
> To see the artificial in manure."

Julius Hensel.

Hermsdorf unterm Kynast.

9

APPENDIX

CONTRIBUTIONS FROM OTHER SOURCES

STONE-MEAL.
By Herm. Fischer, M.D., Westend, Charlottenburg.
From No. I of Pomologische Monatshefte, 1892, Edited by Friedrich Lucas, Director of Pomological Institute in Reutlingen.

Not only those who like to eat fruit and vegetables, but much more those who raise fruits and vegetables, rejoice in the abundant and savory produce of our gardens. To maintain this produce and, if possible, to increase it, is the endeavor of rational horticulture. This end is striven for through careful cultivation, and more especially by abundant manuring, especially with nitrogenous compounds. I say this end is striven for, but it is not always reached. The long-continued labors of a well-known investigator, Julius Hensel, have opened new prospects for agriculture, fruit raising and horticulture; they show, in fact, how we can "turn stones into bread." Hensel's book, *Das Leben*, has lately appeared in a second edition. Every thinking reader will find a high enjoyment in the study of this book. For our present consideration I recommend especially Chapter XXX, p. 476, *Agriculture and Forestry.* Lately a little work, by the same author, has appeared on *Mineral Manure the Natural Way for Solving the Social Question,* published by the author at *Hermsdorf unterm Kynast,* Silesia. The first part of the pamphlet is devoted to the defensive, for like all pioneers our author meets with violent opposition from the orthodox teachers of agriculture, whose cues and periwigs have come into a great state of agitation.

After his defense the author passes to his theme proper. Earth, air, water and sunlight must co-operate to produce a fruitful growth. We entrust our seeds to the earth. What is the "earth?" The earth or soil is disintegrated primitive rock (gneiss, granite, porphyry). The soil of our fields is continually being increased by the disintegration of primitive rocks, and from this there grow up grasses, herbs, shrubs and trees; without mineral constituents no plant can grow. Now, when in level plains the upper layer of the soil through long cultivation has become exhausted of certain necessary mineral constituents new rocky material must be provided, from which nothing has as yet been grown, which, therefore, still contains all its strength; this is not only the most natural, but also the simplest and at the same time the cheapest way to increase and maintain the yield of our fields. This is not mere theory, thought out in the study; but experience and success have demonstrated it. With Hensel there is no more need for experiments, but merely of demonstration. A firm in the Rhenish Palatinate has produced a variety of fertilizers, according to his directions, out of pulverized rocks, such as are most suitable for the various plants. I will here only mention fertilizers for vineyards, meadows and potato fields. Hundreds of advocates affirm the favorable results of these fertilizers. The rest should be read in the pamphlet itself.

Since the spring of 1890 I have used stone-meal manure in my garden, situated on our well-known sandy soil, and am extraordinarily well pleased with the results. I have, e.g., picked from a row of raspberry bushes about twenty-three yards long fifty quarts of the most delicious fruit, some of over one inch in length and three-fourths of an inch in diameter. The shoots of this year, which will bear next year, are as thick as a finger, some as thick as a thumb, and up to eight feet high. The young fruit trees planted about three years ago are bearing very well, and what is well to notice they are set abundantly with buds for blossoming next year. What is especially surprising is that I have found no worms at all neither in my raspberries nor my early pears and apples; the winter apples also have so far not shown a single worm-eaten fruit. My vegetables I sowed in furrows, covering first with mineral manure and leveling the furrow with earth. The plants I took out to transplant have a mass of roots such as I have never seen even in a manure bed. They, therefore, were easily transplanted; none withered. I will not mention my asparagus because the variety used (Horburger Riesenspargel) of itself brings great shoots. I have cut asparagus weighing six to nine ounces; they were a foot long and their circumference at the middle of their length was four and one-half inches; the taste of this asparagus is excellent. I would especially point to the quality, the most delicious savor of fruits, etc., grown with this manure in contradistinction to those grown with stable manure; this is also shown in the pamphlet mentioned above. With all these advantages mineral manure is even cheaper than all other artificial manures. "We need no artificial manure if we supply that which we annually draw from the soil in form of fruits, etc., by means of fresh, unexhausted pulverized granite, gneiss or porphyry as the genuine strengthening and primitive fertilizer, mixed with gypsum and lime."

How the fungus of the grapevine, the *Odium tuckeri*, is to be removed and how even the phylloxera can be extirpated and, according to Hensel's statements, has been extirpated, may be seen in *Das Leben*, p. 478.

The fallacy of the supposition hitherto held that all cultivated plants must have especially nitrogenous food in order that they may prosper becomes more and more apparent. By experiments it has been indubitably proved, and Hensel always asserted, that plants, and especially the leafy, leguminous fodder plants (clover, vetches, etc.), can take up and elaborate nitrogen through their leaves out of the air just as the carbonic acid taken up from the air is worked up into hydrocarbons under the operation of light. All we need, therefore, is to furnish the soil with the necessary mineral constituents. Mineral manure is the most profitable, most lasting and, what is not to be overlooked, an entirely odorless fertilizer.

If I shall have succeeded in calling the attention to the reader to the glorious effects of this manure, the object of these lines is attained. When the use of this manure is then followed by surprising results the beautiful fruits will, in the most literal sense, be my reward.

STONE FERTILIZING.
By Dr. Emil Schlegel, Pract. Physician in Tubingen.
From the Wegweiser zur Gesundheit, Sept. 15, 1891.

This is a subject that does not immediately concern the *Wegweiser zur Gesundheit*, but which nevertheless on account of its far extended importance may have the greatest effect on the well-being and wealth of our people. The chemist, Julius Hensel, of whom we have several times before this spoken in earlier numbers of the *Wegweiser*, and who is known to its readers by his genial book *Das Leben*, has lately published another work which deserves particular mention. He therein sets forth that the loss of soil in mineral substances (lime, magnesia, etc.) is not supplied by animal offal, though this produces a strong forcing of the plants, which makes the leaves and the products weakly and injurious, as this is said to have developed in the irrigated fields at Berlin, where the bones and muscles of the animals fed on their produce are suffering and also the milk is not satisfactory for sucklings. In a still higher degree these injurious forcing substances are found in artificial manures and especially in Chili-nitre, causing a rapid, surprisingly luxurious growth; but when the fruit or the seeds develop there is a manifest falling off. Now, since every year millions of dollars are transferred from the pockets of the farmers into those of manufacturers of artificial manures, and of speculators and stockholders, this amounts to an impoverishment of the soil by parasites.

The true cure of an exhausted soil consists, according to Hensel, in supplying it with comminuted rocks, especially granite, gneiss, porphyry and lime. Thereby the plants receive again what they naturally demand. The *Wegweiser* would here remark that the best proof of these views given on a great scale is thousands of years old; i.e., the fertility of Egypt. The mud of the Nile consists almost exclusively of finely comminuted rocks, with very, very few organic nitrogenous constituents. But the flooded districts owe their unexampled fertility to just this precipitated stone dust. Hensel writes at the end of his book:

"Almost every field contains stones which have only been acted upon in part by the dissolving moisture of the soil, and which therefore shows a more or less rounded form. These stones, as they injure the spade or plow, are usually removed to the sides of the fields and there heaped up, and are then sold at a cheap rate for use on the highways. The farmer who acts thus sells his birthright, so to say, for less than a pottage of lentils, for he removes the source of fertility from his fields. If such stones are heated in the stove or on the hearth for half an hour and then thrown into water they become so friable that they may be broken into small pieces by the hands and may easily be pulverized with a hammer." It is to be wished that these developments of Hensel should find a wide diffusion."

LETTER TO MR. SCHMITT.
Oranienburg, August 17, 1893.

Dear Honored Sir:

I have just safely returned from my long tour for the stone-dust, having been away five weeks, and I herewith give you a brief report, so that you may also enjoy the victory which stone-dust has gained wherever it has been really put to a practical test.

I have already written to you of the eminent, happy effects of stone-dust on the estates of *Count Chamare*. I have been able to see its good effects also in Upper Silesia, and have established there two more stations for the future, where normal trials will be made. I saw exceedingly significant results from stone-dust on the field of *Chief Bailiff Donner* at Culmsee, in West Preussen; i.e., excellent wheat, sowed after barley and oats, with only five hundredweight of stone-dust to the acre; also splendid rye in fourth succession on five hundredweight of stone-dust, and sugar beets following sugar beets on merely six and a half hundredweight to the acre, which promise a very good yield. Here it was found that the fields needed above all a good supply of lime, and this lime was the best support to the happy effects of the stone-dust. On this account the cultivation of the field with stone-meal demanded a simultaneous application of lime of sixteen to thirty hundredweight per acre.

So great a quantity will not be used *in one year*. For the stone-meal made according to Hensel's direction contains as much lime and magnesia as the average crops call for.

The cultivation of sugar-beets can be doubled by stone-meal. This accomplishment would surely be a great result from stone-meal. Also in West Preussen I have established an experimental station for the proper use of stone-meal on a large estate near Braunsberg, belonging to a Herr von Bestroff. This gentlemen called on me for this purpose also before this in Oranienburg.

I hope that this, my first tour in behalf of stone-meal, has not been in vain, and I intend, God willing, to repeat these tours annually, so as to benefit our great and important cause with all my strength. I am quite confident that stone-dust combined in the proper way with lime will by its practical success carry off the victory.

I shall do my best to carry out the stone-meal experiments on the estates of *Count Chamare* in the most conscientious manner, and hope that God's blessing may rest on this my labor, which I perform gladly for my country.

Otto Schoenfeld,

Director of the Agricultural and Forestry School.

TO THE POMOLOGICAL SOCIETY
"HEIMGARTEN IN BUELACH."
Letter by Mr. K. Utermohlen, Teacher in Leinde

By means of the stone-meal manure of Hensel we shall soon surpass all similar undertakings (co-operative Pomological Association.) If the tree has a sufficiency of this primitive substance under its roots it is not only fruitful, but no more sensitive as to frost and diseases. Nor will it be infested as much by insects, as it will be healthy, having a pure sap. With the usual treatment with manure rich in nitrogen the trees are satiated to repletion, and then it is with them as with men. Their fibres are relaxed, their sap is checked, diseases developed, lice and other vermin infest them, and then we have to sprinkle them with mixtures, cut out wounds, put on wax and pitch, etc. By well preparing the soil with this mineral manure we prevent all these troubles from the start, the trees becomes strong and hardened. It is just as when parents bring up healthy children with solid food. They then have none of these troubles and cares encountered by parents who treat their children perversely.

For the last two years I have seen making various experiments with stone-meal manure, and indeed with the different kinds. From my experience with it I have come to the firm conviction that we need no other manure at all but this. I wish I could speak with angels' tongues to make clear to you its great importance for our cause. It would carry me too far to speak of all the various experiments. A radical reform in this direction will have to be made. If we give the trees when they are first planted some of this manure between their roots, with good irrigation, they will be twice as strong and vigorous as without it. We do not need any stable manure to loosen the ground, that is best effected by diligent hoeing and digging. Where this should prove insufficient we call in peat moss to our aid, and this can be gotten cheap here. That is what I did here with my heavy garden soil, and then with the help of stone-meal I have raised the finest vegetables, though the garden has seen no stable manure for eight years. And then how pleasant and cleanly is this mineral manure when compared with the smell of solid and liquid stable manure. Then we should consider its great cheapness. Much can be done with 1 cwt. If we had always to use stable manure we would have to give out great sums every year, and even then we could not get a sufficient quantity. But there must be manure, for "From nothing nothing comes," as the saying is. In this trouble the mineral manure is our best help. We cannot in this matter give any consideration to the authorities in horticulture, as they are in error with respect to the nutrition of plants, I refer especially to their silly theories about nitrogen. Who brings to the strong oaks of one hundred years growing on rocky soil, or to the other lovely children of mother earth out in free nature, liquid or solid manure or sewerage? They grow and flourish and revel in their healthy growth just because they are spared all these. So it will be with our fruit trees when we shall nourish them in a natural manner. It is not a mere secondary question but a most fundamental one which is here involved. The question is whether we shall in the treatment of our little trees follow the perverted and worn-out routine of the wisdom of the professors of our state with their theories of albumen, or whether we will follow the path of nature. We have chosen for ourselves and our mode of living the latter course; it is then surely proper to do the same with respect to our plantations.

If I only had a photographic apparatus I should like to send you a picture of some of our standard trees and some of our half-standards, so that you could convince yourself with your own eyes of the excellent effects of this wonderful fertilizer. This is especially the case with a four-year-old half-standard to which I have specially applied this manure. Such a multitude of the finest russets! It would hardly be thought possible in a little tree of four years. And then you should see how this little fellow has increased in thickness! His coat has almost become too narrow for him. The apples hang twice as thick as in other years, and their flavor can hardly be recognized; their aroma is really refreshing. The same I have perceived this year in our cherries and raspberries. When I come to see you I shall bring a whole selection of apples for trial. I well manured a bed of several square yards of ground and planted it with cucumbers.

After gathering this summer a whole basket full I thought I had a remarkably good crop but now the bed is just as full again, although I have picked some from time to time. The same is the case with the beans and onions which I have noticed particularly, as we can only plant flat-rooted vegetables between the trees.

We cannot sufficiently express our satisfaction that we have in this manner not only found a substitute for, but something far better than stable manure.

THE STONE-MEAL OF DR. HENSEL BEFORE THE COMMITTEE ON FERTILIZERS OF THE GERMAN AGRICULTURAL SOCIETY.

(From Dr. F. Schaper, in Nauren, in the Osthavellaendisches Kreisblatt.)

"Most of the members evidently knew nothing about the mineral manure save through the abuse of the well-known Professor *Wagner*, in *Darmstadt*. It is a sad state of affairs, but it is true, that these institutions, founded for the use of agriculture, cannot act freely, but have to regard quite different groups of interest; i.e., those of the manufacturers of manure. That their interests and those of the farmers are directly opposed to each other is manifest from this that farmers desire cheap fertilizers, but the manufacturers of manure desire to keep them as high as possible in order that they may make the more money. Now the agriculture trial stations receive part of their support from the manufacturers of manures, as they are paid for their control-analyses, experiments, etc. In order that they may not lose these contributions these institutions must avoid whatever runs counter to the interests of their employers. It is often even stipulated in the contracts between the manufacturers of fertilizers and the agricultural trial stations that they should obligate themselves to protect these factories of artificial manures from unfair competition.

But who is to decide who and what belongs to "unfair competition?" The manufacturer will be apt to consider every one as an "unfair competitor" who threatens to diminish his profits, and he will therefore insist, and a certain plausibility cannot be denied to their demands, that the agricultural stations according to their contract should in every case work for them. This enables us to explain the silence or the open hostility of the agricultural trial stations as to stone-meal manure. No intelligent man will on this account consider this hostility of importance or take too serious a view of it.

This opposition should even be of use to the cause, since no truth valuable in itself can be injured by the exercise of a criticism ever so sharp, if this is done in a scientific manner. But such an objective criticism has not been exercised on Hensel's theory, but certain directors of trial stations, instead of combatting it in a scientific manner, have descended to gross abuse and have, therefore, been judicially punished.

Mr. *Shulz-Lupitz*, the chairman of the Committee on Fertilizers, objects to Mr. Hensel, in the sessions of 14 February of this year (1893), that he is conducting his cause against acknowledged men of science in a rough manner, and that this could not be rebuked sufficiently—a peculiar objection as coming from a man who, so far as the direction of the proceedings and the form of the resolution offered by him and finally accepted to go to show, has only a slight regard for the whitewashed politeness of Europe. He has, we are sorry to see, forgotten that Mr. Hensel was not the attacking party, but quite a different set of people, the close friends of Mr. Shulz-Lupitz, and the aim of the proceedings was evidently to get them out of the scrape into which their own precipitation had brought them. The well-known professor, *Dr. Wagner*, in Darmstadt, director of the agricultural trial station there, in his edict in the year 1889 had called the mineral manure a gross swindle and denied to it any value. This edict had been published by Zimmer's factory in Mannheim in innumerable pamphlets and in journals as a supplement. Thus it came that in far extended agricultural circles which only heard of mineral through journals of *Wagnerian* tendency Mr. Hensel was accounted a charlatan. When a man like Mr. Hensel who thinks he has discovered something useful for agriculture is thus shamefully reviled, and in the end deals with his assailants in a somewhat doughty fashion, who will account him reprehensible? Now Mr. Schulz-Lupitz in the proceedings continues this kind of polemics against Mr. Hensel.

The resolution passed declares in its first part: *"Hensel's stone-meal is from the standpoint of practical and scientific knowledge to be designated a worthless fertilizing agent."* Just the contrary is the truth. From the standpoint of practical experience the stone-meal has shown itself a valuable fertilizer surely enough, the men who had some practical experience in the manure were not acknowledged by these gentlemen of the manure division but they were presented by some learned men of this assembly (Latin economists Uncle Braessig would probably call them) conscious of their infallible book learning, as men who could easily be cheated, and who now also cheat others, thus as cheating and cheated.

These learned gentlemen seem to forget that in practical life a grain of common sense outweighs a hundred weight of book-learning, as the shepherd of the Abbot of St. Gall said long ago.

In the second part of its resolution the manure division rebukes the "impertinent bearing" of the "so-called chemist" Hensel with indignation and "expresses to Mr. Professor Wagner, in Darmstadt, the thanks of the practical agriculturists for his appropriate designation of the stone-meal of Hensel. This later gentlemen had called it as above mentioned, a gross swindle." The manure division has cautiously avoided using this expression. For this expression has caused the punishment of two editors who had copied the Wagnerian production and its author. Professor Wagner has escaped a probable judicial condemnation only by the fact that the complaint owing to an oversight fell under the statute of limitation.

We who are convinced of the value of Hensel's method of improving the soil look trustingly into the future, with conviction that truth has always made its way if it only found courageous and intelligent champions.

I would, therefore, request all who have had any practical experience with the stone-meal to publish their experiences for the good of the cause and of their fellowmen, and not to leave the field to the sole occupancy of the opponents. The word of the *single* man easily dies away, the *multitude* only makes the full chorus, especially in our democratic times, and this chorus alone can hush the short-sighted in violence and the self-interests which oppose the new discovery.

ABOUT STONE-MEAL MANURE.
(Land und Hauswirthschaftliche-Rundschau)

No. II, 1893

A short time ago we published an article on the experiments with the new stone-meal fertilizer; we also gave space to an objective presentation as to the causes which make stone-meal suitable for a manure. The new fertilizer and its discoverer have suffered severe infestations. It may, therefore, interest our readers to see a report from our neighborhood as to some trials made of it. We have received the following: Sometime ago a burgomaster of the neighborhood called our attention to the splendid stand of grain manured with stone-meal on the "Stenheimer Hof," on the estate of the Grand Duke of Luxemburg. A company of gentlemen who take an earnest interest in this matter (chemist, Dr. *Edel*, teacher *Eeisenkopf*, and the landed proprietor, *Loeillot de Mars*, from Wiesbaden; Director *Spiethoff*, editor of the *Pioneer*, from Berlin; Mr. *Forke*, of Eleville, and Dr. *Dietrich* and Dr. *Brockhues*, from Oberwallauf) in a Whitsuntide excursion verified these statements beyond all expectations. In spite of the great drouth the rye on 18 1/2 acres of ground had stout stalks and long thick ears, and the tenant, Mr. Heil, told us that little more than 5 hundredweight to the acre, altogether 100 hundredweight, had been used. Just as luxuriant with dark green stalks and leaves stood the oats, 1 1/2 acres, right by the highway. This piece of ground had not had any stable manure for many years, and had only received 20 hundredweight of stone-meal with an addition of 6 hundredweight of iron slag. The comparison with neighboring fields which had been well cultivated but differently manured, was very much in favor of the manuring with stone-meal. Just as striking as was the success of Mr. Forke on his rye, oats and clover, it was on his fruit trees and grape vines. We would only mention that a clover field of which one-half had been manured with stable manure and the other half with stone-meal showed a dense growth of clover. A cherry tree and a tree with Gravenstine apples, which for many years had yielded no fruit worth speaking of, this year, after having been well supplied with stone-meal, are covered over and over with fruit.

A neighboring farmer told him, on seeing his fine oats, "Here we can see clearly how your manure acts; it could not stand better if you had put on 60 cartloads of stable manure per acre, which would have cost $125 to $150 per acre.

The condition of the grape-vines after repeated manuring with stone-meal was on comparison with other grape-vines found to be excellent, but we shall return to particulars, as with the rye and oats, at the time of harvest. We invite the farmers of the neighborhood to make their comparisons and to convince themselves of the solid results of manuring with stone-meal. This possesses the quality of *vigorously nourishing the plants and making them strong to resist frosts and drouth*. The above-mentioned gentlemen will bear record as to whether Hensel is really the "false prophet" that he has been represented to be.

To Director Spiethoff this investigating committee, in which he took part, was the more wished for, as the *Pioneer* had first called attention to the scientist Hensel, and had also been the first to communicate last year the astonishing results in the Agricultural School of Oranienburg.

WHAT HELP CAN BE GIVEN TO THE HARD-PRESSED FARMERS.
(Badischer Volksbote, July 1, 1893.)

This question is the most important in our national affliction of drouth, and the lack of pasturage connected therewith, that can occupy any true friend of his country. And this question is not answered by old party catchwords of protective tariff and free trade and monopoly; it will neither be solved in the *Reichstag* nor in the local legislature, though legislation is also in this matter an important factor. The farmer alone can decide here; in his hand lies the future of our people. The matter at stake is the most valuable possession a people can have, their native land and soil. These are faring ill. Our land is not only being more heavily encumbered with mortgages every year, but is also losing some of its good qualities and fertility, and as the debt increases the value decreases. This is the most threatening complication we have to meet. But there is no use in merely lamenting it, it must be improved and amended. And it can be improved if we will only open our eyes and see and learn and act in accordance with that which we learn.

We can improve the soil and make it fertile by using stone-meal as a fertilizer as is shown by the experience of many practical farmers. In the *"Neues Mannheimer Volksblatt,"* M. A. Heilig publishes the following declaration:

"The Landwirthschaftliche Blaetter," by Mr. Councillor *Nessler*, in Karlsruhe, rejected a few months ago Hensel's method of mineral manuring. Whoever wants to convince himself how Hensel's acts in practice is invited to inspect my two and one-half acres of barley near the Isolating Hospital. Despite the unusual drouth the barley has attained an unusual height, and stands much fresher than the barley in other fields. After the harvest I shall have the yield determined before witnesses to see the difference also in this respect."

When practical experiments show such results the farmer ought to give up his old prejudices and try himself whether the new method of manuring is not better than the old. That the scientists and professors ignore the new source of fertilizing need not astonish us, on the contrary: "The professors are opposed to it, therefore it is good," may soon become a proverb, for hitherto the professors have always opposed everything good at its first appearance. We think Hensel's method of manuring will likely make agriculture again profitable, and we shall recommend it even if all should oppose us on this account. When at some future date, not too far removed, the German farmer and through him all the German people shall enjoy the blessings of this improvement of the soil we shall yet receive thanks that we helped to prepare the path for this new good during its hard times.

FROM *THE RHEINISCHER COURIER*, WIESBADEN, JUNE 6, 1893.

We have received the following communication: "In No. 152 of your valued journal, among the 'Agricultural Communications,' is a short, but favorable notice, from the Manure-Division of the 'German Agricultural Society,' concerning stone-meal. With respect to this, permit me to invite you and every one interested to examine the fields and vineyards of my friend Franz Brodtmann here, as also the rye fields of Mr. Heil, the tenant farmer at Hof-Steinheim, on the estates of the Grand Duke of Luxemburg, which had been manured with this material according to my directions, and they will be convinced that contrary to these views stone-meal is a most important fertilizer of the very best quality, which when rightly used yields the best results."

Respectfully,
L. Forke

Eleville, June 4, 1893

FROM *THE RHEINISCHER COURIER*, JUNE 29, 1893.

Communication No. 175 of your morning edition of June 26 contains an attack on stone-meal as a manure, and an exaltation of the present method of manuring with potassa, nitrogen and phosphoric acid. I was for many years an adherent of this latter method, But I have become convinced by experience and practical trials that these artificial manures serve indeed to *force the growth* and may be used with effect for several years, but that they do not restore to the soil what we withdraw from it in cultivation. Therefore the state of our soil unavoidably deteriorates from year to year, and at last refuses its service. Nobody can stand partridges every day, but he can his daily bread, and so it with all plants, which not only need potassa, nitrogen and phosphoric acid for their nourishment, but in addition soda, lime, magnesia, sulfuric acid, silicic acid, chlorine, iron, fluorine, carbonic acid, etc. All these elements are found in many rocks in greater or smaller quantites, and Hensel cannot be sufficiently thanked that he has pointed out to us farmers these inexhaustible supplies. When we return stone-meal to the soil we restore to it all that was in the soil from the beginning, and that our early ancestors did well with the original material is manifest as stable manure has only been used for about two hundred years, and so-called artificial manure only about fifty years. Of course we cannot force matters with stone-meal; but if it is brought on the fields in autumn and plowed under we may count on success as may clearly be seen here and as I have already stated in No. 155 of your much valued paper. With all esteem for science, we farmers cannot be contented with simply finding out how much potash, nitrogen and phosphoric acid and the artificial fertilizers contain and how much every percent thereof costs, we must rather strive to raise good crops on our fields with slight expense, without at the same causing our soil to deteriorate by a one-sided system of fertilizing, and this is certainly done when we only apply potassa, nitrogen and phosphoric acid.

L. Forke

Eleville, June 27, 1893

FROM *THE NEUES MANNHEIMER VOLKSBLATT*, JULY 19, 1893.

That the much-abused stone-meal cannot be without its excellent points the results in the fields best show. Mr. Kircher here has raised on various fields manured with this material barley and wheat, which must absolutely convince even the most skeptical of the usefulness of this manure. First, not only are the stalks considerably higher and stronger than those from fields manured with other material, but the ears are on the average one-third longer and the grains considerably more perfect. (Mr. Kircher has left in the editorial room of the "N.M.V." several wheat ears and barley ears from his fields to show the difference, also some from neighboring fields which have not been manured with Hensel's fertilizer. Whoever is interested in this matter, and every farmer should be so, may inspect the ears in our office.)

IRON SLAG.
(Koelnische Volkszeitung, April, 1893, No. 234, First Sheet.)

The supplement of the *Thueringer Landboten* brings a noteworthy article by the practical farmer, A. Armstadt, under the heading: "The Future of the Iron Slag." The author first notes that iron slag has risen to be the most generally used fertilizer containing phosphoric acid only in consequence of an immense amount of advertising, but now it seems to be about to lose much of its reputation. Even the German Agricultural Society will earnestly declare against it in its next publication. "I myself," says A. Armstadt, "have never been enabled to feel any enthusiasm for iron slag in consequence of my experiments with it, and I have frequently on various occasions declared this, and it is a satisfaction to me that numerous reports are now appearing which confirm my observations. First of all, the fact that people come to doubt the theory of a gradual enrichment of the soil thereby will cause it to lose credit. Men of science, as is well known, gave out the notion that the soil must gradually be enriched with phosphoric acid in order that rich crops may be raised. Iron slag was said to be the most suitable for this purpose, not only because the phosphoric acid in it is cheapest, but also because phosphoric acid in this form would in time become more soluble. But most farmers have waited probably in vain for the after effects. I myself have never found any after effects. According to the latest experiments, it is not only probable but pretty well established that every enrichment of the soil with phosphoric acid in mineral form is a waste, for it passes into a form difficult of solution, so that it cannot any longer be taken up by plants. Prof. Dr. Liebscher (Goettingen) even found that with a manuring of 100 hundredweight of iron slag to three-fifths of an acre no after effects developed, though he waited for it for seven years. But the copious applications of iron slag are founded on this theory of enrichment only.

NEUES MANNHEIMER VOLKSBLATT, AUGUST 3, 1893.

With a few potted plants or a small piece of garden any one can make a trial of the value or worthlessness of Hensel's teaching, and no more paper need be wasted in their justification. An increasing number of farmers are experimenting successfully with the new fertilizer and it will gradually but surely supersede the old. The old manures supplied plants with too much *forcing* material and too much phosphoric acid, a substance which surely causes plant-lice, caterpillars, snails and the like. The stone-meal improves the nutrition of the plants without forcing them, so that while their leaves have a lesser amount of water, the fruits and stalks a greater amount of lime and are more wholesome and nourishing. As the fruits mature the phosphorus passes mostly into the seeds and the silica into the leaves and stalks. When agriculture hitherto built its theory of manuring on the ashy constituents of the seeds with their high contents of phosphorus it did not consider that the whole growing plant before the separating process during ripening requires quite different proportions of admixture than what may be derived from the seeds alone. A comparison of Hensel's views on the domain with the question of human nutrition rises very naturally. Exhausted men also are favored with allowing them to eat heartily of the convenient meat, with eggs and milk, all nutriments fully prepared for assimilation. The consequence is an excitation and irritation of the whole organism, bad digestion, increased watery contents of the body, perspiration, thirst, exhaustion from slight exertions, debility. A strong manuring with predominantly animal offal is for plants planted in a soil deficient in certain minerals what a predominantly animal diet is for men. If we look at men who live in the country almost altogether on food difficult of assimilation of bread, vegetable and fruit, we observe a far more quiet bodily activity, little perspiration, little thirst, great and continuous muscular power. It is similar with plants when we offer them again their original nutriments, direct them to the appropriation of mineral constituents and give them organic manures or nitrogen only in small quantities and as a secondary matter. In both cases the constitution will be more normal, freer from parasites (diseases). If we notice in agricultural journals the enormous expenditures for advertising artificial manures it may be known what a gain these factories yield, and the mind grows sad at the wealth withdrawn from German farmers, who even without this are so hard pressed.

Dr. E. Schlegel,
Pract. Physician, Tuebingen.

WIENSBADNER GENERAL ANZEIGER, JULY 8, 1893.

For diminishing the distress as to fodder, we do not need as the troubled farmer is advised in another journal, to use artificial manure: superphosphate and Chili-nitre or superphosphate of nitrate of potassa for the meadows; superphosphate of nitre with acid phosphate or with phosphate of lime for the cloverfields; fresh stable manure and liquid manure, Chili-nitre, superphosphate of potassa or superphosphate of nitre for Indian corn for the horse, etc. The pen and compositors object to the twenty-fold repetition of the wonderful compounded fertilizers. We recommend for the meadows, ashes of every kind, and for the root fields, street dust, and in general for the future, mineral manure, which is at the same time the best protection against drouth and all the diseases of plants, as it gives to plants the power of resistance and which in turn is transferred to men and animals through their food. That the diminution of the present and also of any future distress as to fodder may be effected by mineral manure is demonstrated by the following experience:

For five years I have been using stone-meal manure in my garden and fields. The results always have been satisfactory in every respect, for the soil becomes better every year by using this manure. Especially this year during the extraordinary drouth, the excellent effects of stone-meals fully manifested themselves. The flower as well as the different vegetables developed so magnificently that every one who passed my garden stopped and admired the great growth, especially of the Kohlrabi. In the cabbage which I planted at the beginning of April in my cow pasture, the rich crop is the more astonishing as it was not watered during the whole of its growth, this field has received *for five years only stone-meal manure (no solid or liquid stable manure);* alongside of the cabbage field is the potato patch and it shows a most luxurious growth *despite of the abnormal drouth.* The above experience has brought me to the firm conviction that this fertilizer not only improves and augments the cultivated soil, but also keeps it moist and therefore prevents the rapid drying up of plants during a drouth.

Bernth. Wettengel,
Horticulturist and Truck Farmer

Frankenthal, July 1, 1893.

MOERSCH, NEAR FRANKENTHAL, JUNE 30, 1893.

For two years I have used stone-meal manure with the greatest success, and especially this year, *despite the extraordinary drouth.* The result has been magnificent; the barley showed a much larger yield of grain than ever before; the potatoes were very fine and to our astonishment remained *untouched by the heavy frosts,* though others that had received stable manure suffered very severely. I was very much pleased with the effects on oats and clover. *Quite astonishing also is the dark green, full leaved appearance of the sugar beets, notwithstanding the great continuous drouth.* With the fruit trees where I especially applied the new fertilizer, I have fully learned how extraordinarily it acts. I would therefore urgently recommend every farmer to adopt the new method. With the greatest satisfaction. I sign myself

Peter Heilmann,
Agriculturist

THE UNDERSIGNED FARMERS

In order to determine the results of the new method of fertilizing, the undersigned farmers and friends of agriculture assembled on June 25, 1893, early in the morning at 7 o'clock sharp, for a common inspection of the fields, and at this occasion we inspected the following fields within the domain of Frankenthal:

Names of fields.	Planted with.	By the farmers.
Muhlegewann,	Potatoes,	Carl Heilman, 1.
New Gardens,	Barley,	Conrad Bender, widow.
Grosse Garkueche,	Barley,	Peter Huber, widow.
Grosse Garkueche,	Rye,	Adam Mack, 1.
Rohrlache,	Barley,	Daniel Scherr.
Kleiner Wald,	Barley,	Valt. Zimmerman.
Kuhweide,	Potatoes and cabbage,	Bernhard Wettengel.
Schiesshaus,	Barley,	The rifle club.
Actien-Eiskeller,	Potatoes,	The stock club.
Gartengewann on the right hand of Wormserstr,	Barley,	Clem. Wurmser.
Gartengewann on the right hand of Wormserstr,	Rye,	Wilh. Schwarz.
Gartengewann on the right hand of Wormserstr,	Barley,	Jah. Mees.
Erbbestand,	Barley,	Hen. Grueming.
Gartengewann on the left hand of Wormserstr,	Barley,	Phil. Schatz.
Mittelgewann,	Barley,	Joh. Bender, widow.
Spiegelgewann,	Barley,	Valt. Zimmermann.
Wingertsgewann,	Potatoes,	A. Gensheimer.
Wingertsgewann,	Potatoes,	Jac. Armbrust, fieldguard.
Neuweide,	Sugar-beets,	Pet. Diehl, Beindersheim.
Neuweide,	Sugar-beets,	Conr. Peters, Beindersheim.
Pfaffengewann,	Barley,	J.L. Braunsberg, II.
Pfaffengewann,	Potatoes,	Phil Schatz.

Nearly all taking part in the inspection were practical farmers, who are entirely familiar with the local relations and quality of the fields. The result of the inspection may well be called astonishing.

Though the summer has been abnormally dry, all the barley inspected was distinguished by its dark green appearance when compared with other fields not fertilized with stone-meal. The ears compared with the others contained more rows. In a number of them we counted forty grains extraordinarily fine and well developed. The same conditions existed with the rye. The potato fields showed a surprising luxuriant stand. We must especially mention the full leaved dark green appearance of the sugar-beets, which encourages us to look forward to a full development of the roots. With the cabbage the rich crop is the more surprising as it has not been watered during the whole period of its growth.

The undersigned have taken part in this general inspection with the more interest, as they are convinced that the violent dispute concerning the new method of manuring can only be decided by practical success. This was the reason why they desired to determine the numerous results obtained by a general local survey made in the above mentioned way in a conscientious manner, and they believe that they have thus ministered to the common good.

Biendersheim: *P. Diehl*; Edigheim: *H. Jaeger, Jean Loosmann*; Flowersheim: *C. Garst, Ph. Schreiber*; Frankenthal: *J. Armbrust, Fr. Bender, J. Fries, J. Fueschsle, K. Gaschott, G. Kirchner, C. Luehel, H. Mayer, J. Mees, C. Moeller, C. Rupp, Ph. Senatz, D. Scherr, Fr. Scheuermann, G. Wettengel, Jos Zimmermann*; Friesenheim: *Chr. Moersch: P. Heilmann* ; Oppau: *W. Claus.*

AFTERWORD

Uranus is the third largest of our planets. It is a huge ball of frozen hydrogen, methane and ammonia. It also—according to astronomers—has a rock core. It is so far from the sun that one year on Uranus is equal to 84 years on earth. It is close enough to earth, however, to be seen on a clear night with the naked eye.

Of the five satellites of Uranus, one is very peculiar and so faint that it could not be seen clearly until Voyager II made a fly-by of Uranus and its five moons. The faint moon is called Miranda.

Photos sent back by Voyager II showed Miranda to be a huge rock with deep wide furrows on its surface. The cliff side of many walls of the deep valleys are of solid ice. It is a very strange configuration for any moon!

Astronomers speculate that at one time, in the distant past, that Miranda had a solid rock core covered with a solid mantle of deep ice—sort of a world covering glacier. According to theory, in the far distant past, an asteroid whammed into Miranda and it shattered into a million little rocks and ice cubes. Over the eons it is beginning to reassemble, due to force of gravity, and is in a middle growth of its final rock core, ice covered configurations. In short, the ice in these cliffs is rising to the top and the rock is sinking. In my opinion it is a very good theory . . . except!

Except it is one more example of either/or science. Why is gravity alone responsible for the reassembly and reformation growth of Miranda? Since water is *diamagnetic* and rock *paramagnetic* (one of the + & -, or yen and yang of life) why should not these magnetic antenna forces be at work along with gravity?

I never seem to emphasize enough that paramagnetism is *not* magnetism. Rather it is the ability of a substance to collect or resonate to the magnetic fields of the cosmos. A paramagnetic antenna collects the alternating waves of cosmic magnetism. It is an antenna force.

It is quite true that the ice which is light would rise to the surface above the heavier mass of rock. It is also true that, since opposites attract, and ice is diamagnetic (repelled by a magnet) the ice would bind to the rock core in a solid mantle, just as in its present mid-point of reassembly the ice face clings to the rock cliffs that make up Miranda's deep furrows.

It is astonishing to me that not only is the paramagnetic force not mentioned by astronomers, the word does not appear in the *Astronomer's Handbook*, but so also is it overlooked by soil scientists. This despite the fact that most rock is of volcanic origin and all good soil, which erodes from rock, is paramagnetic.

Every farmer I have ever worked with, from my youth pitching peas and cutting cabbage, to my USDA-university days, has a field, or large "spot," which is hopelessly inadequate for growing even healthy weeds.

When about twenty years ago I started worrying about the health of weed killer insecticide—poisoned plants, I noticed that if I held a magnet to a glass tube of good soil it would jump to the magnet, whereas a glass tube of poor soil would hardly move to the magnet. These farmers' poor spots, or "hopeless back 40s," always demonstrated low cgs readings.

Over the years, in over twenty countries and thirty or so states in the U.S. I have measured this force, first with a magnet and later with a Barrington cgs meter. CGS means centimeters, grams per second, or how *much* will go *how far* in *one second*. It is the physical measure of the paramagnetic antenna force and is listed for the elements in the *Physics Handbook*. Oxygen, a gas, is highly paramagnetic with a reading of over 3000 cgs. I reasoned that since all plant life and water is diamagnetic and all excellent soil paramagnetic, that this must be yen and yang of plant growth.

I soon began to measure stone religious structures around the world, pyramids, round towers, stone rings and megalithic "tombs." I have yet to measure one that does not read 300 cgs or above. The blue stone of Stonehenge is 500 to 600 cgs, the pink granite of the Kings Chamber of the Great Pyramid in Egypt 400 to 500 cgs.

Some limestone is diamagnetic and some slightly paramagnetic, 10 to 30 cgs, however, it is volcanic rock that holds the paramagnetic antenna property so vital to agriculture. That of course does not mean that one does not need lime in the soil, only that organic matter and lime is not enough. If the paramagnetic antenna force is not strong enough to attract the alternating magnetism of the earth's surface and cosmos, then the crops will be weak and the plant "immune" system will be down. Sick plants, like sick people, will give off excessive ammonia and ammonia is a "pump" chemical for scents from people or plants.

Ammonia plus body odor attracts flies and mosquitoes, ammonia plus cotton or corn scent attracts moths and weevils that feed on plants. Put fermenting beer or fruit juice outside sometime and see how many night flying moths you can attract. Fermentation is a matter of degree so the more sick the plant the more ethanol and ammonia given off, and therefore the stronger the infrared frequencies (photons) emitted from the plant scent. There is a Callahan formula for healthy plants:

lots of organic matter
good soil aeration
lots of soil organisms   = healthy plant = no insects or disease
high paramagnetism

low organic matter	= lots of ammonia
compacted soil and soil organisms	= pumped scent molecules
dead soil organisms	= attracted insect & disease
low paramagnetism	

It goes without saying, of course, that well aerated soil, even though low in paramagnetic antenna force, will be better than compacted soil since oxygen has a cgs of 3000. However, without eroded rock paramagnetic soil, the plant may well look healthy, but will not be healthy enough *not* to attract insects.

It has become obvious to me that the ancient megalithic people knew about the rock forces and utilized them for healing and farming.

The megalithic "stone age" period is divided into paleolithic (old stone age), mesolithic (middle stone age) and neolithic (new stone age) periods. The mesolithic people were hunters, fishers, and gatherers. The farming cultures, which revolutionized mankind's life, began in the neolithic age. According to archaeologists, who may or may not be correct (much guessing), the neolithic people crossed over from Europe some time before 4000 B.C. and besides farming, devoted a good deal of their energy to building great stone "tombs" called megaliths (big stones). These so called *court, passage* and *wedge* tombs are scattered all over Ireland. Not four miles from Magheramenagh Castle, where I spent all of my overseas duty in World War II, at a place called Killy Beg, is a "village" of wedge "tombs." Near our radio station on a region called Keenaghan is a spot called Blackrock, which is an overgrown wedge tomb.

Although a few jars of ashes have been taken from the so called "tombs," they are most certainly not "tombs." Is a European Gothic Cathedral a tomb because a hundred famous people or monks may be buried in the walls and floors? I would have to answer *no!*

Court "tombs" are rock lined earth mounds with a low wall in front of them. Passage "tombs," of which Newgrange in Ireland is the largest, are shaped just like a Gothic Cathedral (cross shaped), and wedge tombs are open and fan shaped, flared out in the front. Wedge "tombs" were built around 2000 B.C. or before. There are over 400 in Ireland. They all face between south and west so that the sun shines in the front opening of the wedge where they are broader and higher. In other words, the ancients wanted the sun to shine into the rock vault throughout most of the day in far north Ireland. All are built of highly paramagnetic rock, granite, basalt, etc. They were, without a doubt, small rock healing and meditative caves. They were, and still are, resonant cavities for collecting the sun's magnetic energy and the radio waves from the sun-stimulated atmosphere. These long wave radio frequencies come in at dawn and dusk and I can now detect them with a moist sandstone or limestone rock. While hard, non-porous rock, like granite, works best for collecting the magnetic energy, porous water soaked rock, like sandstone, works best for collecting the long wave radio frequencies.

When I first pointed out, years ago, that such rock structures were magnetic and electromagnetic (radio) antenna-detectors I was considered "out of it" by biologists and physicists alike. We now know that amorphous, non-crystalline materials (which soil and rocks are) make very excellent semi-conductors.

Some of the best solar cells and semi-conductors are now made of amorphous glass. Such highly efficient amorphous detectors, glass semi-conductors, were first made by S. R. Ovshinsky in the late 60s. The early crystal set, which I mention in my boyhood story, *Soul of the Ghost Moth*, is of course an amorphous (rock) semi-conductor. Long before Ovshinsky, and the scientists who scorn my work, were around, common sense should have told them that rocks make good amorphous semi-conductors.

Amorphous semi-conductors, such as my damp limestone and sandstone radio frequency antenna-detectors, have certain unique properties, two of which are low energy elementary excitation, and photoinduced (sunlight) reversible structural change. This, besides the fact that atoms move in them by *tunneling*, which is the main physical mechanism of all semi-conductors.

Although I can increase the signal strength of my red sandstone amorphous detector by fifteen times by putting it inside a model megalithic tomb, I can increase it up to twenty-five times by putting it inside a model Navajo hogan. Both are diamagnetic-paramagnetic resonant cavities.

Anyone who knows the Navajo character understands that no Navajo curing chant can be carried out except *inside a hogan* by the Navajo medicine man.

There are two types of Navajo hogans. The older type was built of logs, cedar and juniper, and covered completely with a mound of earth. The more modern one is of log, hexagonal-shaped with a heavy clay soil roof, as illustrated. Hogans have diamagnetic walls and paramagnetic roofs (yen and yang) a perfect resonant cavity for the dawn and dusk resonant radio frequencies of soil and plant life. I did not first discover the necessity of having volcanic rock in one's soil. Long before I was born, that astute agriculturalist Julius Hensel tried his best to convince the German farmer that without volcanic rock soil, there could be no healthy crop growth. He was speaking to a public, then and still, brainwashed by pure chemical agriculture. In short, he was over a hundred years ahead of his time when he wrote *Bread from Stones.*

It is a rare privilege for me to add my chapter to this marvelous book and to lend my intellect to a further appreciation of what this caring German accomplished for mankind. I am proud that my present work outlines the scientific mechanism of exactly why the amorphous stone of megalithic tombs, and the soil of Navajo hogan roofs work. The antenna resonant properties of soil, round towers, rock structures and Indian hogans are not speculations of archaeologists but experimental facts.—*Philip S. Callahan*

INDEX

INDEX

argillaceous slate, 43
Armbrust, J., 74, 75
Armstadt, A., 70
aroma, 61
arterial blood, 14
arteries, ossified, 12
artificial fertilizers, 26, 45, 69
artificial manure, 26, 45, 50-52, 57,
   62, 68, 69, 72
ash, 25, 27, 37, 38, 40-43, 48, 51,
   72, 79
ash of barley, 37
ash, beech, 37
ash, dried, 37
ashes, peat, 29
ashes, tobacco, 37
ashes, vegetable, 28
ashes, wood, 38
ashy constituents, 14, 20, 23
asparagin, 33
asparagus, 33, 56
asteroid, 76
asthma, 18
astronomers, 76
Astronomer's Handbook, 77
atmosphere, 32
atmospheric nitrogen, 29
atmospheric vapor, 48
atoms, 34
augmenter of fertility, 50

bacilli, 22
bad digestion, 71
Badischer Volksbote, 66
Balkan countries, 45
Balkan, 22
bark, 43
barley, 7, 10, 25, 59, 67, 69, 73-75
barley ears, 70
Barrington cgs meter, 77
baryta, ethyl sulfate of, 33
baryta, sulfate of, 33
basalt, 80
base, ammoniacal, 30
base, phosphate, 29
base, sulfuric, 29

Basel, 48
basic constituents, 45, 47, 51
bean straw, 41
beans, 3, 28
beans, field, 40
beech ashes, 37
beech leaves, 37
beech trees, 48
beeches, 3, 38
beechwood, 43
beer breweries, 43
beeves, 43
Beindersheim, 75
Bender, Conrad, 74
Bender, Fr., 75
Bender, Joh., 74
Berlin, 10, 22, 57, 65
Bestroff, Herr von, 59
The Bible, 47
Biel, 48
biologists, 80
birches, 3, 38
Birkenfeld, 43
Blackrock, 79
blood, 35, 49
blood, arterial, 14
blood-disks, 15
Bohemian Mountains, 45
bone-black, 43
bony substances, 52
Braessig, Uncle, 64
Braunsberg, II, J. L., 59, 75
bread, 72
Bread from Stones, cited, ix, xviii,
   81
breweries, beer, 43
Brockhues, Dr., 65
Brodtmann, Franz, 68
brown oxidation, 11
buckwheat, 10
Bulgarian, 22
burdocks, 45
burned-up substances, 48
bushes, 34
bushes, raspberry, 55
butter, 16

frequencies (photons), infrared, 78
frequencies, radio, 80
Fries, J., 75
Friesenheim, 75
frost, 60, 66, 73
fruit, 28, 34, 44, 45, 48, 54, 55, 57, 65, 71, 72
fruit trees, 44, 56, 61, 66, 74
Fueschsle, J., 75
fungi, 44
fungus, 56
The Future of the Iron Slag, 67

G. L. Privy Councillor, 46
Garst, C., 75
Gartengewann on the left hand of Wormserstr, 74
Gartengewann on the right hand of Wormserstr, 74
Gaschott, K., 75
gas, 78
gases and minerals, balance of, x, xi, xv
gases, cycling of, x
gases, greenhouse, xii, xiv, xvi
Geest rocks, 50
gelatine sugar, 33
General Anzeiger fur Schlesien and Posen, 9
Gensheimer, A., 74
German Agricultural Society, 13, 62, 68, 70
Germans, 51, 52
German farmers, 67, 72
German tobacco, 38
Germany, 49
Germany, Palatinate of, 39
glacial gravel, xviii
glacier, 76
glass, amorphous, 80
Glauber's salt, 14
glycolic acid, 26
gneiss, 7, 10, 22, 38, 45, 55, 56, 58
gneiss, Virginian, 38
God, 36, 44, 59
Goettingen, 71

good soil, 77
gooseberries, 10
gout, 18
grain, 16, 28, 36, 48, 49, 51, 70, 73, 75
grain, California, 14
grain, lodged, 45
grain, lodging of, 14
grain, Western, 14
grain, wheat, 41
Grand Duke of Luxemburg, 65, 68
granite, 3, 7, 9-11, 22, 38, 42, 43, 45, 46, 55, 56, 58, 80
granite, pink, 78
grapes, 29, 44
grapevines, 44, 56, 66
grass, 16, 34, 35, 43, 55
gravel, glacial, xviii
Gravenstine apples, 66
gravity, 76, 77
greenhouse gases, xii, xiv, xvi
Grosse Garkueche, 74
growers, tobacco, 37
growth, plant, 78
Grueming, Hen., 74
guano, 3
guano, fish, 29, 30
Guben, 17
Gulf of California, xiii
gypsum, 6, 7, 22, 56

H_6O_3, 21
Haemus Mountains, 45
Hamaker, John D., x-xviii
Hamburg, 43
hard soap, 48
hares, 51
hay, 16, 20
hay-worm, 44
healthy and unhealthy produce, 9
healthy crops, 7
healthy plant, 78
heat, 47
hedge, 31
Heil, Mr., 65, 68
Heilig, M. A., 67

Land und Hauswirthschaftliche-
  Rundschau, 65
Landshut, 10
The Landwirtschaftliche Blaetter,
  67
The Law of the Minimum, 1
lead, oxide of, 48
leaf-lice, 23
leaf, Virginia, 38
leaves, 34, 41, 42, 44, 47, 57, 65, 71
leaves, beech, 37
leaves, dried, 37
leaves, tobacco, 14
lechithin, 28
leguminous plants, 3, 40, 42
leguminous fodder plants, 56
Leinde, 60
Leipzig, 52
leucin, 15, 21
level regions, 50
lice, 60
lice and sewage, 22, 23
Liebig, 41, 51
Liebig's mistake, 41
Liebscher, Dr., 71
life, ocean, xi
life, plant, 78, 81
life, soil, 81
The Life, xxi
light, 57
lime, 2, 5-7, 9, 10, 11-17, 21, 25,
  29, 32, 34, 37, 38, 40-42, 45, 47,
  48, 50, 51, 56-59, 69, 71, 78
lime, carbonate of, 11, 13, 22, 34,
  39, 44
lime, fluorate of, 33
lime magnesia, 38
lime, oxalate of, 32
lime, phosphate of, 14, 33, 43, 72
lime and sheep, 17
lime, sulfate of, 14, 19, 11
lime, syenite, 38
limestone, 78, 80
limestone, secondary fossiliferous, ix
linen, 45
linen factories, 43
linen, French, 11

linen, Silesian, 11
linen, Spanish, 11
linseed, 10, 40
linseed oil, 32
liquid manure, 14, 20-22, 49, 61, 72
liquid stable manure, 61, 73
lodged grain, 45
lodging of grain, 14
Loeillot de Mars, 65
Loewenberg, Kreis, 9
Loosmann, Jean, 75
low paramagnetism, 79
Lucas, Friedrich, 54
Luehel, C., 75
lymphatic fluid, 49
lymphatic glands, swelling of, 18
lymphatic vessels, 34

Mack, Adam, 74
Magheramenagh Castle, 79
magnesia, 2, 5-7, 9, 10, 11-17, 25,
  29, 33, 34, 37-42, 44, 45, 47, 48,
  50, 51, 57, 59, 69
magnesia, carbonate of, 11
magnesia, lime, 38
magnesia, sulfate of, 14, 33
magnetic, 77
magnetic antenna, 77
magnetic antenna detectors, 80
magnetic energy, 80
magnetic fields, 77
magnetism, 77
magnetism, alternating, 78
magnetism, cosmic, 77
The Makrobiotic, , xxi, 17, 18
malnutrition, xiv, xvi
manganese, 6, 7, 33, 40, 44, 45, 47,
  48, 50, 51
manganese, oxide of, 33, 34
Mannheim, 63
mantle, solid, 76, 77
manure, 3, 15, 19, 20-23, 38, 44,
  45, 47, 49, 50, 56, 57, 60-62, 64-
  66, 68, 69, 71, 73
manure, animal, 45

murrain, 18
mustard, 40

N_2, 21
$N_2H_{12}O_6NH_6O_6$, 33
N_2H_6, 21
$N_2H_6O_3Fe_2 = N_2H_6Fe_2O_3$, 48
natural fertilizers, 44
Nauren, 62
Navajo, 81
Navajo hogan, 81
Navajo medicine man, 81
needles, dried pine, 37
nematodes, 44
neolithic (new stone age), 79
nerve fat, 7
nervousness, 18
Nessler, Mr. Councillor, 67
Neues Mannheimer Volksblatt, 67, 69, 71
Neuweide, 75
New Gardens, 74
Newgrange, 79
Nile, 43, 55
Nile mud, 43
nitrate of potash, 15
nitrate of potassa, superphosphate of, 69
nitre, superphosphate of, 72
nitrogen, 2, 3, 4, 7, 18, 21, 23, 27, 29, 32, 43, 44, 47, 48, 50, 51, 56, 60, 61, 68, 69, 72
nitrogen, atmospheric, 29
nitrogenous, 51
nitrogenous ammonia, 23
nitrogenous compounds, 54
nitrogenous constituents, 58
non-porous rock, 80
Norman breed horses, 12
nutrious elements, 43
nutritive crops, 41
nutritive plants, 49
nutritive supplies, 43

oaks, 3, 38, 61
oakwood, 43

oats, 7, 10, 59, 65, 66, 73
Oberwallauf, 65
ocean life, xi
Odium Tuckeri, 56
offal, animal, 72
oil, 28, 48
oil crops, 28
oil, almond, 32
oil factories, 43
oil, linseed, 32
oil, olive, 32
oil, oxidized, 48
oil plants, 43
oil, poppy, 32
oil, rapeseed, 32
oil-bearing plants, 40
oil-producing seeds, 40
oil-yielding plants, 42
oils, vegetable, 32
oleic acid, 3, 48
olive oil, 32
Oppau, 75
opposition to stone meal, 60
Oranienburg, 58, 59
organic manures, 72
organic matter, 78
orthopedic institutes, 52
ossification, 12
ossified arteries, 12
Osthavellaendisches Kreisblatt, 62
Our Diseases and Our Remedies, 18
Ovshinsky, S. R., 80
oxalate of lime, 32
oxalic acid, 31, 32
oxalis, 32
oxen, 50
oxidation, 34
oxidation, brown, 11
oxide of iron, 2, 33
oxide of lead, 48
oxide of manganese, 33, 34
oxidized oil, 48
oxidized water, 31
oxidizing respiration, 34
oxygen, 14, 18, 27, 31, 32, 48, 78, 79

potassa-alum, 13
potassa, muriate of, 25
potassa, phosphate of, 12, 16, 51
potassa, superphosphate of, 72
potassa, sulfate of, 5
potassium, xviii
potato patch, 73
potatoes, 3, 28, 73-75
potato fields, 55
potted plants, 71
powdered iron slag, 39
precipitation, xvii
Preussen, West, 59
primary rocks contain, 6, 7
primitive fertilizer, 56
primitive manure, 43
primitive rocks, 55
Privy, G. L., 43
process of growth, 32
products, aeriform, 48
propylamin, 30
Prussian *morgen*, 52
Prussian Vierraden, 14
putrefaction, 15
pyramids, 78

quartz, 29
quicksilver, 48
quinces, 44

radio frequencies, 80
radio waves, 80
rain water, 29, 31
rape, 28
rapeseed, 40, 45
rapeseed oil, 32
raspberries, 61
raspberry bushes, 55
red sandstone amorphous detector,
  80
reed-grass, 25
regions, Java, 48
regions, level, 50
Reichstag, 66
religious structures, 78

remineralization, xvii, xviii, xix
resonant cavitity, 80, 81
resonant properties, antenna, 81
respiration, 49
respiration, oxidizing, 34
Rheingan, 44
Rheinischer Courier, 68
Rheinprovinz, 44
Rhenish Palatinate, 55
rheumatism, 16, 18
Rhine vineyards, 41
Riesengebirge, 15
rifle club, The, 74
ring, stone, 78
rock, amorphous, 80
rock core, 76, 77
rock dust, xviii
rock lined earth mounds, 79
rock, mass of, 77
rock meal, 45
rock, marble, 10, 11
rock material, disintegrated, 47
rock, non-porous, 80
rock, paramagnetic, 80
rock, porous water-soaked, 80
rock soil, volcanic, 81
rock structures, 81
rock vault, 80
rock, volcanic, 78, 81
rocks, 22, 76, 77, 80
rocks, comminuted, 58
rocks, Geest, 50
rocks, primitive, 55
Rohrlache, 74
roof, paramagnetic, 81
root fibres, 26, 29
root fields, 72
roots, 39, 42, 43, 45, 48, 51, 56, 60
roots of burdocks, 48
roots of willows, 48
roses, 22, 44, 45
Rothenzechau, 10
round towers, 78, 81
Rupp, C., 75
russets, 61
Russia, 52

rust, 44
rye, 7, 9, 10, 48, 65, 66, 68, 74, 75

saline, 26
salt, 15, 25
salt, Epsom, 14
salt, Glauber's, 14
salt, Strassfurt potash, 39
sandstone, 80
sandy soil, 29
sap, 60
Savage, Albert Carter, ix, xviii
scarlatina, 51
scent, corn, 78
scent molecules, 79
scent, plant, 78
Schaper, Dr. F., 62
Schatz, Phil, 74, 75
Scherr, Daniel, 74, 75
Scheuermann, Fr., 75
Schiesshaus, 74
Schlegel, Dr. Emil, 57, 72
Schoenfeld, Otto, 59
Schreiber, Ph., 75
Schreiberhau, 15
Schwarz, Wilh., 74
scrofula, 18, 51
sea water, 26
seaweed, 25, 26
sedge, 25
seed-vessels, 28
seeds, 40, 41, 51, 55, 57, 71
seeds, oil-producing, 40
semi-conductors, 80
semi-conductors, amorphous, 80
Sempach, 12
Senatz, Ph., 75
serpentine, 38
settlers, European, 49
sewage and lice, 22, 23
sewerage, 61
shale, oil, ix
shave-grass, 25
sheep and lime, 17
sheep's-yarrow, 10
sheep, 43

shepherd of the Abbot of St. Gall, 64
shoots, 29, 44, 56
shrubs, 55
Shulz-Lupitz, Mr., 62, 63
sick plants, 78
Sierra Nevada, xiii
sign of the cancer, 3
Silesia, 9, 55
Silesia, Upper, 59
Silesian linen, 11
Silesian marble, 10
silex, 38
silica, 7, 41, 42, 45, 48, 51, 71
silica alumina, 38
silicated potash, 39
silicates of potash, 33, 39
silicates, 2, 24, 26, 34, 35, 38
silicea, 35
silicic acid, 2, 5, 6, 9, 25, 26, 40-42, 47, 69
silicium, fluoride of, 2
sine qua non, 50
slag, iron, 7, 11, 44, 65, 70, 71
slate, argillaceous, 43
slate, hornblende, 38
snails, 71
soap, hard, 48
soaps, 2, 48
soda, 3, 5, 6, 9-11, 13-15, 22, 25, 29, 33, 34, 37-40, 42, 45, 47, 48, 50, 51, 69
soda, sulfate of, 14, 16
sodium, chloride of, 7
soil, 78, 80, 81
soil aeration, 78
soil, calcareous, 23
soil, compacted, 79
soil, cultivated, 73
soil, excellent, 78
soil, good, 77
soil life, 81
soil, moor-land, 29
soil, paramagnetic, 79
soil, poor, 77
soil, sandy, 29
soil, Virginia, 14

solar cells, 80
solar forces, 34, 35
solid ice, 76
solid manure, 20, 22, 49, 61
solid mantle, 76, 77
solid stable manure, 61, 73
The Solution to Our Pesticide Problem, xviii
Soul of the Ghost Moth, 80
sour-worm, 44
Spanish flax, 11
Spanish linen, 11
species, extinction of, xvi
Spiegelgewann, 74
Spiethoff, Director, 65, 66
spring-worm, 44
stable manure, 14, 15, 17, 18, 20, 21, 23, 38, 43, 44, 45, 50, 51, 60-62, 65, 66, 69, 72, 73
stalks, 41, 48, 51, 65, 69, 71
Stamm, Dr., 12
starch, 16, 28, 32, 48
stearic acid, 3
stearine candle, 31, 48
stems, 41, 42
Stenheimer Hof, 65
stock club, The, 74
stone age period, megalithic, 79
stone, amorphous, 81
stone dust, xxiii, 27, 52, 58, 59
stone-dust manure, 47
stone fertilizing, 57
stone-meal, 18, 20, 23, 24, 26-28, 45, 54, 59, 62, 63, 65-69, 71, 73, 75
stone-meal fertilizer, 62, 65
stone-meal manure, 45, 47, 55, 60, 63, 65, 73
stone rings, 78
stone tombs, 79
Stonehenge, 78
Strassfurt potash salt, 39
straw, 41, 45, 51
straw, oat, 37
straw of field bean, 41
straw of poppy, 41, 42
straw of winter wheat, 41

straw, bean, 41
straw, poppy, 41
straw, wheat, 41
street dust, 72
strong food, poison food, 17
structures, religious, 78
structures, rock, 81
substances, bony, 52
substances, burned-up, 48
substances, combustible, 48
substances, mineral, 40
substratum, ammoniacal, 33
sugar, 16, 25, 28, 32, 33, 43, 48
sugar, gelatine, 33
sugar-beets, 3, 5, 6, 28, 59, 74, 75
sulfate of ammonia, 3, 5, 22
sulfate of baryta, 33
sulfate of lime, 11, 14, 19
sulfate of magnesia, 14, 33
sulfate of potassa, 5
sulfate of soda, 16
sulfate, 5, 25, 34, 44
sulfur, 7, 12, 15-17, 35, 47, 50, 51
sulfuric acid, 5-7, 9, 12, 29, 37-42, 48, 69
sulfuric base, 29
sun, the, 25, 34, 36, 47, 48, 76
sunlight, 28, 55
sunshine, 35
superheated melt, xi, xii
superphosphate, 3, 7, 72
superphosphate of nitrate of potassa, 72
superphosphate of nitre, 72
superphosphate of potassa, 72
supplies, nutritive, 43
The *Survival of Civilization,* x
Sweden, 30
Swiss Alps, 17
Switzerland, 12
syenite, 38
syenite lime, 38
synthetics, xvi
system, tectonic, xi, xii, xv

Peptones (Leucin and Tyrosin